A Stanley Gib
Thematic Cat

COLLECT
FUNGI ON STAMPS

John-Paul Greenewich

First Edition, 1991

Stanley Gibbons Publications Ltd.
London and Ringwood

By Appointment to Her Majesty The Queen
Stanley Gibbons Ltd., London
Philatelists

Published by **Stanley Gibbons Publications Ltd**
Editorial, Sales Offices and Distribution Centre:
5 Parkside, Christchurch Road, Ringwood,
Hants BH24 3SH

For "Isis"
With Love

—

First Edition — June 1991

© Stanley Gibbons Publications 1991

ISBN 0-85259-293-0

Item No. 2890 (91)

Printed in Great Britain by Pardy Printers Ltd., Ringwood, Hampshire

Fascinating Fungi

Fungi are single-celled or filamentous organisms belonging to the group Mycota. Until recently they were, together with bacteria and algae, regarded as non-vascular plants. Now, however, they are treated as a separate kingdom, distinct from both plants and animals. Unlike green plants they lack chlorophyll, so cannot manufacture their food by photosynthesis. Fungi have been in existence for at least 600 million years and there are now estimated to be between 250,000 and 300,000 species, the largest of which, *Rigidoporus ulmarius* (the Elm Fomes), can exceed 400 cm in circumference.

Filamentous fungi are made up entirely of microscopic threadlike structures called hyphae. In most species these develop into a dense network (mycelium) which permeates the organic matter on which they feed. Nutrients are obtained by the secretion of digestive enzymes. Many species reproduce sexually by releasing spores from a specialized structure called a fruiting body. These fruiting bodies, of which mushrooms and toadstools are familiar examples, are produced when two compatible mycelia of the same species band together and the hyphae grow and expand rapidly by absorption of water. Other fungi reproduce asexually by simple division.

Fungi are found in every habitat throughout the world, including the sea. They have a remarkable capacity to survive in adverse conditions, some being able to scavenge essential nutrients from the atmosphere. Those which are lichenized are pioneers of terrestrial habitats (see Lichens). Saprophytic fungi occupy an important place in the ecosystem by assisting the process of decomposition, while mycorrhizal species effectively underpin the ecology of temperate forests (see Mycorrhizas).

Excavations in China indicate that Man has been using fungi as food for at least 6,000 years. In Western Europe we have come to regard mushrooms and other fungi as a delicacy (e.g. truffles) though baking, brewing and the manufacture of wines and spirits all depend on yeast, a single-celled fungus, for fermentation. Elsewhere fungi are an important source of nutrition. When Charles Darwin visited Tierra del Fuego, for example, he discovered that the staple diet of the local people largely consisted of a golf ball-shaped fungus called *Cyttaria*.

Sir Alexander Fleming's discovery of Penicillin in 1928 heralded perhaps the most important medical application for fungi to date, although their use in folk medicines dates back at least 1,000 years. The styptic properties of a number of species are particularly well documented and as late as 1940 a puff-ball called *Bovista* was being used to cure an injured leg thought to need amputation. In America Shii-take extract (*Lentinus edodes*) has recently been approved for clinical trials against AIDS.

Antipathy towards fungi derives in part from those species responsible for spoilage and disease. Most plant diseases are caused by fungi and those which affect crops are a major agricultural hazard. They include smuts, rusts, mildews, blights and scabs. Honey Fungus is a notorious parasite of trees. In higher animals and Man the most prevalent fungal infections are ringworm and thrush.

Although many fungi are good to eat confusion with other species may lead to severe and sometimes fatal poisoning. The collecting and eating of certain species may be an offence under The Wildlife and Countryside Act or the Misuse of Drugs Act so that when collecting fungi the importance of expert advice cannot be over-emphasized. Anyone interested in wild food should join a foray organized by the British Mycological Society or a local Natural History Society.

About This Book

This catalogue is a listing of stamps depicting mushrooms and other fungi on stamps issued by countries throughout the world. It is based on the Stanley Gibbons *Stamps of the World Simplified Catalogue,* published annually in three volumes. It contains over 650 stamps which depict around 350 species of fungi. The first supplement containing new issues not in this catalogue appeared in the March 1991 number of *Gibbons Stamp Monthly.*

What is included

All issues, including overprints and surcharges, depicting fungi scientifically or artistically, their study and cultivation as listed in the *Stamps of the World Catalogue.* Miniature sheets are included when they contain stamps different from those in the regular stamp sets.

What is excluded

All stamp variations of watermark and perforation which are outside the scope of *Stamps of the World.* The lists also exclude stamps depicting imaginary species (e.g. in animations, illustrations from children's literature, fairy/folk tales and children's paintings) as well as fungi used as emblems (e.g. the Girl Guides Association). Stamps listed in the Appendix in *Stamps of the World* will be found in similar sections in the countries listing.

Countries Section

This section lists in alphabetical order, with prices, the various countries and territories which have issued stamps depicting fungi. Within each country or territory the stamps are listed in chronological order with the year of issue and catalogue number taken from the *Stamps of the World Catalogue.*

Fungal nomenclature can be bewildering – some species have been known by more than one systematic (mycological) name and common names may vary in different parts of the world. In this section fungi are identified by their systematic names only. If the systematic name applied by the issuing authority is now obsolete its successor is quoted in brackets.

Fungal Species Section

This section lists all the species which have appeared on catalogued stamps in systematic (mycological) order. Under each entry are given,

in alphabetical order (a) systematic synonym(s), if any, (b) English name (s), if any, (c) the countries and catalogue numbers of the stamps which depict that particular fungus.

Lichens and Mycorrhizas

The association of fungi with other organisms is the subject of two additional sections. The first is a listing of Lichens on stamps (i) in order of issuing country and (ii) in systematic order. The second is a listing of mycorrhizal associations by tree for both trees and fungi which are depicted on stamps.

Acknowledgments

I should like to thank Prof. D.L. Hawksworth and Dr. D.W. Minter of the International Mycological Institute, Dr. D.N. Pegler of the Royal Botanic Gardens, Kew, and the British Mycological Society's librarian, Dr. B.L. Brady, for their help and advice. I am especially grateful to Dr. M.O. Moss of the University of Surrey who, despite extensive commitments, has generously undertaken to check the systematic listing, helped with identification and guided me through the more esoteric regions of mycology.

Finally I should like to thank Joy O.Y. Phillips whose special love and encouragement have made the difference to me and this little catalogue. Comments and criticism will be greatly welcomed in order that future editions may better serve the interests of thematic collectors.

References:-

Hawksworth, D.L., Sutton, B.C. and Ainsworth, G.C. (1983). *Ainsworth & Bisby's Dictionary of the Fungi.* The International Mycological Institute, Kew.

Ing, B. (1976). Fungi on Stamps. *Bulletin of the British Mycological Society* No. 10 pp 32–37.

Moss, M.O. and Dunkley, I.P. (1981). More Fungi on Stamps. *Bulletin of the British Mycological Society* No. 15 pp 61–63.

Moss, M.O. and Dunkley, I.P. (1984). Fungi on Stamps 1980–1984. *Bulletin of the British Mycological Society* No. 18 pp 134–138.

Moss, M.O. and Dunkley, I.P. (1986). Fungi on Stamps 1984–1985. *Bulletin of the British Mycological Society* No. 20 pp 63–68.

Moss, M.O. and Dunkley, I.P. (1988). Recent Issues of Postage Stamps Depicting Fungi. *The Mycologist* (2) pp116–121.

Trappe, J.M. (1962). Fungus Associates of Ectotrophic Mycorrhizae. *Botanical Review* Vol. 28 pp 538–606.

Books on Fungi

INTRODUCTORY AND GENERAL BOOKS

A Passion for Mushrooms, Antonio Carluccio
Introduction to Modern Mycology, J.W. Deacon
Fungi – Folklore, Fiction and Fact, W.P.K. Findlay
The Mushroom Feast, Jane Grigson
Ainsworth & Bisby's Dictionary of the Fungi, D.L. Hawksworth, B.C. Sutton and G.C. Ainsworth
Mr. Jackson's Mushrooms, H. Jackson and M. Cazort
Mushroom Magic, Michael Jordan
Fundamentals of the Fungi, E. Moore-Landecker
Mushrooms for Color, M. Rice and D. Beebee
Introduction to Fungi, J. Webster

FIELD GUIDES

The Mushrooms and Toadstools of Britain and North-western Europe, Marcel Bon et al.
Collins New Generation Guide to Fungi of Britain and Europe, Dr. Stefan Buczacki
Poisonous Plants and Fungi, M. Cooper and A. Johnson
Lichens: An illustrated guide, F.S. Dobson
A Guide to Mushrooms, Michael Jordan
Lichens: An illustrated guide, F.S. Dobson
A Guide to Mushrooms, Michael Jordan
Mushrooms and Toadstools, a field guide, Geoffrey Kibby
Mushrooms and Fungi, A Hamlyn Colour Guide, Dr. Jaroslav Klán
Collins Guide to Mushrooms and Toadstools, Morten Lange and F. Bayard Hora
The Oxford Book of Flowerless Plants, B.E. Nicholson and Frank H. Brightman
Mushrooms and Toadstools, D. Pegler

Mushrooms and Other Fungi of Great Britain and Europe, Roger Phillips
Mushrooms and Toadstools, Donald Raynor
Mushrooms and Toadstools, Derek Reid
A Complete Book of Mushrooms, Augusto Rinaldo and Vassili Tyndalo
Identification of the Larger Fungi, R. Watling

SPECIFIC SPECIES

The Bird's Nest Fungi, Harold J. Brodie
Genera of Hyphomycetes, J.W. Carmichael et al.
British Fungus Flora 3–Bolbitiaceae: Agrocybe, Bolbitius and Conocybe, D.M. Henderson, P.D. Orton and R. Watling
Amanita of North America, D.T. Jenkins
The Genera of Myxomycetes, G.W. Martin, C.J. Alexopoulos and M. Farr
British Fungus Flora 4–Pluteaceae: Pluteus and Volvariella, P.D. Orton
The Genus Lentinus, D. Pegler
Keys to the British Species of Russula, R. Raynor
The Polyporaceae of North Europe (2 vol.), L. Ryvarden
British Fungus Flora 5–Strophariaceae and Coprinaceae, R. Watling and N.M. Gregory

Societies

The British Mycological Society welcomes anyone with an interest in fungi. There are three categories of membership and details are available from:

The Membership Secretary,
British Mycological Society,
c/o The International Mycological Institute,
Ferry Lane,
Kew, Richmond,
Surrey, TW9 3AF

In addition to meetings, the Society organizes forays and workshops and all members receive a quarterly magazine, *The Mycologist*, which aims to promote mycology to a wide readership.

Do you remember the Jonathan Miller TV documentary about Clive, the musician who cannot remember anything for more than a few seconds?

Many thousands of people have permanent and serious memory disorders after brain injury. Clive's wife, Deborah Wearing, founded AMNASS in 1986 to help other patients, their families and the professionals who work with them.

With the help of the country's leading experts AMNASS provides information and advice to members, runs workshops and seminars, raises public awareness, lobbies for better treatment and care and is developing a network of self-help groups.

The problem is huge. The office and resources are tiny. Please help. Covenant forms are available or please send a cheque payable to The Amnesia Association to:

AMNASS

The Amnesia Association
St. Charles' Hospital
Exmoor St
London W10 6DZ
081-969 0796

Countries Section

Arrangement

The various countries and territories are listed in the same order as in *Stamps of the World*. Those few which are not in alphabetical order are covered by cross-references. Each entry includes the geographical location and details of the currencies used. The dates quoted against these currencies are those on which they were first used for stamps in this catalogue.

Illustrations

These are three-quarters of actual size. One design from each issue is depicted, but only those overprints and surcharges required for identification are included.

Listings

These are divided into years by dates and into individual issues by the illustrations.

For philatelic details the *Stamps of the World*, or the 22 volume standard catalogue, should be consulted.

A † against the catalogue number indicates an issue where unlisted stamps in the set depict designs other than fungi.

Miniature sheets are indicated by a **MS** prefix.

Prices

Those in the left-hand column are for unused stamps and those in the right-hand column for used.

Issues where all the designs depict fungi are priced as sets only; single stamps and those from "broken" sets are priced individually.

Our prices are for stamps in fine average condition, and in issues where condition varies we may ask more for the superb and less for the sub-standard.

The prices of unused stamps are for lightly hinged examples for those issued before 1946, thereafter for examples unmounted mint.

Prices for used stamps refer to postally used examples, though for certain issues they may be for cancelled-to-order.

The minimum price quoted is 10p which represents a handling charge rather than a basis for valuing common stamps.

The prices quoted are generally for the cheapest variety of stamps, but it is worth noting that differences of watermark, perforation, or other details, outside the scope of this catalogue, may often increase the value of the stamp.

All prices are subject to change without prior notice and we give no guarantee to supply all stamps priced. Prices quoted for albums, publications, etc. advertised in this catalogue are also subject to change without prior notice.

Guarantee

All stamps supplied by us are guaranteed originals in the following terms:

If not as described, and returned by the purchaser in the original transaction, we undertake to refund the price paid to us. If any stamp is certified as genuine by the Expert Committee of the Royal Philatelic Society, London or by B.P.A. Expertising Ltd., the purchaser shall not be entitled to make any claim against us for any error, omission or mistake in such certificate.

Consumers' statutory rights are not affected by the above guarantee.

AFGHANISTAN

Central Asia
100 poul (pul) = 1 afghani (rupee)

1985

1028	3a	*Tricholomopsis rutilans*
1029	4a	*Boletus miniatoporus* (*Boletus erythropus*)
1030	7a	*Amanita rubescens*
1031	11a	*Boletus scaber* (*Leccinum scabrum*)
1032	12a	*Coprinus atramentarius*
1033	18a	*Hypholoma sp*
1034	20a	*Boletus aurantiacus* (*Leccinum aurantiacum*)

Set of 7   2·50   1·40

ALBUM LISTS

Write for our latest list of albums and accessories. This will be sent on request.

1063† 4a *Suillus luteus* and Green
Woodpecker   10   10

ALBANIA
South-east Europe
100 qint = 1 lek

1971

1444† 15q "The Three Peasants" (Durer)
(one carrying a basket of
mushrooms)   15   10

1990

2450   30q *Amanita caesarea*
2451   90q *Lepiota procera*
2452   1 lek 20 *Boletus edulis*
2453   1 lek 80 *Clathrus cancellatus*
                              Set of 4   75   45

GIBBONS STAMP MONTHLY
finest and most informative magazine for all
collectors. Obtainable from your newsagents or
by postal subscription — details on request.

ALGERIA
North Africa
100 centimes = 1 dinar

1983

844   50c *Amanita muscaria*
845   80c *Amanita phalloides*
846   1d40 *Pleurotus eryngii*
847   2d80 *Terfezia leonis*
                              Set of 4   2·75   1·75

1989

1027   1d *Boletus satanas*
1028   1d80 *Psalliota xanthoderma*
       (*Agaricus xanthodermus*)
1029   2d90 *Lepiota procera*
1030   3d30 *Lactarius deliciosus*
                              Set of 4   1·25   1·00

ANDORRA
Pyrenees Mountains between France and Spain

Spanish Post Offices
100 centimos = 1 peseta

1983

166   16p *Lactarius sanguifluus*   60   1

1984

177   11p *Morchella esculenta*   . . . . .   2·00   2·00

1985

183   30p *Gyromitra esculenta*   40   40

1986

186   30p *Marasmius oreades*   30   30

1987

95   100p *Boletus edulis*   90   90

COLLECT SHIPS ON STAMPS
The largest Stanley Gibbons thematic catalogue
to date — available at £10.50 (p.+ p. £2.75) from:
Stanley Gibbons Publications Ltd, 5 Parkside,
Christchurch Road, Ringwood, Hants BH24 3SH.

1990

217   45p *Gomphidius rutilus*
       (*Chroogomphus rutilus*)   50   25

ANTIGUA
West Indies
100 cents = 1 dollar

1986

1042	10c *Hygrocybe occidentalis* var. scarletina	
1043	50c *Trogia buccinalis*	
1044	$1 *Collybia subpruinosa*	
1045	$4 *Leucocoprinus brebissonii*	
	Set of 4	5·00 4·25
MS1046	$5 *Pyrrhoglossum pyrrhum* . .	6·00 6·00

1989

1313	10c *Mycena pura*	
1314	25c *Psathyrella tuberculata*	
1315	50c *Psilocybe cubensis*	
1316	60c *Leptonia caeruleocapitata*	
1317	75c *Xeromphalina tenuipes*	
1318	$1 *Chlorophyllum molybdites*	
1319	$3 *Marasmius haematocephalus*	
1320	$4 *Cantharellus cinnabarinus*	
	Set of 8	6·50 6·50
MS1321	Two sheets (a) $6 *Leucopaxillus gracillimus;* (b) *Volvariella volvacea*	
	Set of 2 sheets	6·50 7·00

ASCENSION

South Atlantic
100 pence = 1 pound

1983

332 7p *Marasmius echinosphaerus*
333 12p *Chlorophyllum molybdites*
334 15p *Leucocoprinus cepaestripes*
335 20p *Lycoperdon marginatum*
336 50p *Marasmiellus distantifolius*
    Set of 5   2·25   2·25

AUSTRALIA

Oceania
100 cents = 1 dollar

1981

823 24c *Cortinarius cinnabarinus*
824 35c *Coprinus comatus*
825 55c *Armillaria luteobubalina*
826 60c *Cortinarius austrovenetus*
    Set of 4   2·10   1·90

AUSTRIA

Central Europe
100 groschen = 1 schilling

1983

1972 5s Symbols of Penicillin V Efficacy
      and Cancer   60   30

BARBUDA

West Indies
100 cents = 1 dollar

1986

Nos. 1042/6 *of Antigua overprinted* **BARBUDA MAIL**
909   10c *Hygrocybe occidentalis* var.
      scarletina
910   50c *Trogia buccinalis*
911   $1 *Collybia subpruinosa*
912   $4 *Leucocoprinus brebissonii*
    Set of 4   5·50   5·50
MS913 $5 *Pyrrhoglossum pyrrhum* . . .   6·00   6·50

1990

Nos. 1313/21 *of Antigua overprinted* **BARBUDA MAIL**
1158   10c *Mycena pura*
1159   25c *Psathyrella tuberculata*
1160   50c *Psilocybe cubensis*
1161   60c *Leptonia caeruleocapitata*
1162   75c *Xeromphalina tenuipes*
1163 $1 *Chlorophyllum molybdites*
1164 $3 *Marasmius haematocephalus*
1165 $4 *Cantharellus cinnabarinus*
    Set of 8   6·50   6·50
MS1166 Two sheets (a) $6 *Leucopaxillus*
      gracillimus; (b) $6 *Volvariella volvacea*
    Set of 2 sheets   6·50   7·00

BELIZE

Central America
100 cents = 1 dollar

1986

962†   5c *Amanita lilloi*   10   10
964†   20c *Boletellus cubensis*   20   20
966†   75c *Psilocybe caerulescens* . . .   70   70
969† $2 *Russula puiggarii* . . . .   1·40   1·40

BENIN

West Africa
100 centimes = 1 franc

1985

992	35f *Boletus edulis*			
993	40f *Amanita phalloides*			
994	100f *Paxillus involutus*			
		Set of 3	1·25	75

BRAZIL

South America
100 centavos = 1 cruzeiro

1984

2106	120cr *Pycnoporus sanguineus*			
2107	1050cr *Calvatia sp*			
2108	1080cr *Pleurotus sp*			
		Set of 3	1·75	60

BHUTAN

Central Asia
100 chetrum = 1 ngultrum

APPENDIX

The following stamps have either been issued in excess of postal needs, or have not been made available to the public in reasonable quantities at face value. Miniature sheets, imperforate stamps etc. are excluded from this section.

1973

Mushrooms. Postage 15ch *Amanita caesarea*, 25ch *Boletus pinicola*, 30ch *Amanita muscaria*, 3n *Lepiota procera*. Air 6n *Cortinarius praestans*, 7n *Clitocybe geotropa*.

BOTSWANA

Southern Africa
100 thebe = 1 pula

1982

533	7t *Coprinus comatus*			
534	15t *Lactarius deliciosus*			
535	35t *Amanita pantherina*			
536	50t *Boletus edulis*			
		Set of 4	4·50	1·60

BULGARIA

South-east Europe
100 stotinki = 1 lev

1961

1274	2s *Amanita caesarea*			
1275	4s *Psalliota silvatica* (*Agaricus silvaticus*)			
1276	12s *Boletus elegans* (*Suillus grevillei*)			
1277	16s *Boletus edulis*			
1278	45s *Lactarius deliciosus*			
1279	80s *Lepiota procera*			
1280	1lev25 *Pleurotus ostreatus*			
1281	2lev *Armillariella* (*Armillaria*) *mellea*			
		Set of 8	3·50	1·10

COLLECT BIRDS ON STAMPS

Second revised edition of this Stanley Gibbons thematic catalogue. Now available at £8.50 (p.+ p. £2.75) from: Stanley Gibbons Publications Ltd, 5 Parkside, Christchurch Road, Ringwood, Hants BH24 3SH.

1987

3408   5s *Amanita rubescens*
3409   20s *Boletus regius*
3410   30s *Leccinum aurantiacum*
3411   32s *Coprinus comatus*
3412   40s *Russula vesca*
3413   60s *Cantharellus cibarius*

Set of 6   3·25   1·40

CAMEROUN
West Africa
100 centimes = 1 franc

1975

750†   15f Polypore (probably *Coriolus* sp)   20   15

BURKINA FASO
West Africa
100 centimes = 1 franc

1985

Nos. 716, 718 and 720/1 of Upper Volta overprinted
BURKINA FASO
744†   25f *Polystictus leoninus* (*Coltricia*
            leonina)   10   10
746†   200f *Phlebopus colossus sudanicus*   90   75
748†   300f *Trametes versicolor* (*Coriolus*
            versicolor) . . . .   1·25   1·00
749†   400f *Ganoderma lucidum* . . . .   1·75   1·40

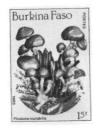

820   15f *Pholiota mutabilis* (*Galerina*
          mutabilis)
821   20f *Hypholoma* (*Naematoloma*)
          fasciculare
822   30f *Ixocomus granulatus* (*Suillus*
          granulatus)
823   60f *Agaricus campestris*
824   80f *Trachypus scaber* (*Leccinum*
          scabrum)
825   250f *Marasmius scorodonius*
826   150f *Armillaria mellea* (air)

Set of 7   3·75   2·00

CANADA
North America
100 cents = 1 dollar

1989

1331   38c *Clavulinopsis fusiformis*
1332   38c *Boletus mirabilis* (*Boletellus*
            mirabilis)
1333   38c *Cantharellus cinnabarinus*
1334   38c *Morchella esculenta*

Set of 4   1·40   1·60

CENTRAL AFRICAN REPUBLIC
Central Africa
100 centimes = 1 franc

1967

133   5f *Leucocoprinus africanus*

134   10f *Synpodia arborescens* (*Marasmius*
      arborescens)
135   15f *Phlebopus sudanicus*
      (*Phaeogyroporus sudanicus*)
136   30f *Termitomyces schimperi*
137   50f *Psalliota sebedulis* (*Agaricus*
      sebedulis)
                            Set of 5   4·00   2·25

1984

1038 5f *Leptoporus lignosus* (*Tyromyces*
      lignosus)
1039 10f *Phlebopus sudanicus*
      (*Phaeogyroporus sudanicus*)
1040 40f *Termitomyces letestui*
1041 130f *Lepiota esculenta* (possibly
      Chlorophyllum esculentum)
1042 300f *Termitomyces aurantiacus* (air)
1043 500f *Termitomyces robustus*
                            Set of 6   3·75   2·50
MS1044 600f *Tricholoma lobayensis* . .   2·75   1·75

1985

1154† 250f Nature studies with fungi . .   1·00   90

CHAD

Central Africa
100 centimes = 1 franc

1985

771   25f *Chlorophyllum molybdites*
772   30f *Tulostoma volvulatum*
773   50f *Lentinus tuber-regium*
774   70f *Lentinus tuber-regium*
775   80f *Podaxis pistillaris*
776   100f *Chlorophyllum molybdites*
                            Set of 6   1·75   1·10

CHINA

Eastern Asia

Chinese People's Republic

100 fen = 1 yuan

1980

2953† 60f "Cabbages and Mushrooms"
       (Qi Baishi)   50   35

1981

3092 4f *Tremella fuciformis*
3093 8f *Dictyophora indusiata* (*Phallus*
      indusiatus)
3094 8f *Hericium erinaceus*
3095 8f *Russula rubra*
3096 10f *Lentinus edodes*
3097 70f *Agaricus bisporus*
                            Set of 6   3·50   1·00

Taiwan
100 cents = 1 yuan

1974

1029 $1 *Agaricus bisporus*
1030 $2.50 *Pleurotus ostreatus*
1031 $5 *Dictyophora indusiata* (*Phallus indusiatus*)
1032 $8 *Flammulina velutipes*
Set of 4   3·50   55

1976

1117† $8 "Two Sika Deer, Mushrooms and Pine" (Fan painting Mou Chung-fu)   75   30

1986

1692† $3 Coral ju-i sceptre with fungus motif   10   10

1987

1735† $2 Silver ju-i sceptre with fungus decoration   10   10

CHRISTMAS ISLAND
Indian Ocean
100 cents = 1 dollar

1984

185 30c *Leucocoprinus fragilissimus*
186 40c *Microporus xanthopus*
187 45c *Trogia anthidepas*
188 55c *Haddowia longipes*
189 85c *Phillipsia domingensis*
Set of 5   3·00   2·25

CISKEI
Southern Africa
100 cents = 1 rand

1987

107 14c *Boletus edulis*
108 20c *Macrolepiota zeyheri*
109 25c *Termitomyces* spp
110 30c *Russula capensis*
Set of 4   55   35

STANLEY GIBBONS
STAMP COLLECTING SERIES
Introductory booklets on *How to Start, How to Identify Stamps* and *Collecting by Theme*. A series of well illustrated guides at low price. Write for details.

1988

217 10f *Termitomyces entolomoides*
218 15f *Termitomyces microcarpus*
219 25f *Termitomyces aurantiacus*
220 30f *Termitomyces mammiformis*
221 50f *Tremella fuciformis*
Set of 6   3·75   1·50

1975

141 16c *Amanita phalloides*
142 30c *Chlorophyllum molybdites*
143 40c *Amanita muscaria*
144 50c *Amanita pantherina*
Set of 4   75   60

494† 60f Sir Alexander Fleming and
Penicillin   70   30

COMORO ISLANDS
Indian Ocean
100 centimes = 1 franc

1985

1978

582 75f *Boletus edulis*
583 125f *Sarcoscypha coccinea*
584 200f *Hypholoma fasciculare*
585 350f *Astraeus hygrometricus*
586 500f *Armillariella* (*Armillaria*) *mellea*
Set of 5   6·00   4·25

613† 200f Sir Alexander Fleming and
Penicillin . . . .   1·25   45

1981

CONGO (BRAZZAVILLE)
Central Africa
100 centimes = 1 franc

1970

827 150f Preparing food (fungi at left) .   70   45

GIBBONS STAMP MONTHLY
finest and most informative magazine for all
collectors. Obtainable from your newsagents or
by postal subscription — details on request.

216 5f *Volvaria esculenta* (*Volvariella*
esculenta)

1985

1007   100f *Coprinus* sp (possibly *Coprinus atramentarius*)
1008   150f *Cortinarius* sp (possibly *Cortinarius mucosus*)
1009   200f *Armillariella* (*Armillaria*) *mellea*
1010   300f *Dictyophora* sp (*Phallus* sp) (possibly *Phallus indusiatus*)
1011   400f *Crucibulum vulgare* (*Crucibulum laeve*)

                Set of 5   4·50   3·00

CUBA

West Indies
100 centavos = 1 peso

1988

3311   1c *Boletus satanas*
3312   2c *Amanita citrina*
3313   3c *Tylopilus felleus*
3314   5c *Paxillus involutus*
3315   10c *Inocybe patouillardii*
3316   30c *Amanita muscaria*
3317   50c *Hypholoma fasciculare*

                Set of 7   1·75   1·25

ALBUM LISTS

Write for our latest list of albums and accessories. This will be sent on request.

1989

3401   2c *Pleurotus levis*
3402   3c *Pleurotus floridanus*
3403   5c *Amanita caesarea*
3404   10c *Lentinus cubensis*
3405   40c *Pleurotus ostreatus* (red)
3406   50c *Pleurotus ostreatus* (brown)

                Set of 6   1·90   1·40

CZECHOSLOVAKIA

Central Europe
100 haleru = 1 koruna

1958

1058   30h *Lepiota procera*
1059   40h *Boletus edulis*
1060   60h *Krombholzia rufescens* (*Leccinum versipelle*)
1061   1k40 *Amanita muscaria*
1062   1k60 *Armillariella* (*Armillaria*) *mellea*

                Set of 5   7·00   1·50

1989

2992   50h *Nolanea verna*
2993   1k *Amanita phalloides*
2994   2k *Amanita virosa*
2995   3k *Cortinarius* (*Leprocybe*) *orellanus*
2996   5k *Galerina marginata*

                Set of 5   1·10   75

DENMARK
Northern Europe
100 ore = 1 krone

1978

665	1k *Morchella esculenta*			
666	1k20 *Boletus satanas*			
		Set of 2	50	35

DJIBOUTI REPUBLIC
East Africa
100 centimes = 1 franc

1980

| 795† | 20f Sir Alexander Fleming and | | | |
| | Penicillin . . . . | | 30 | 10 |

1987

999	35f *Macrolepiota imbricata*			
1000	50f *Lentinus squarrosulus*			
1001	95f *Terfezia boudieri*			
		Set of 3	1·60	1·25

ALBUM LISTS
Write for our latest list of albums and
accessories. This will be sent on request.

DOMINICA
West Indies
100 cents = 1 dollar

1987

1071	45c *Cantharellus cinnabarinus*			
1072	60c *Boletellus cubensis*			
1073	$2 *Eccilia cystiophorus*			
1074	$3 *Xerocomus guadelupae*			
		Set of 4	3·75	3·00
MS1075	$5 *Gymnopilus chrysopellus* . .		2·75	3·00

EAST GERMANY
See under Germany

FALKLAND ISLANDS
South Atlantic
100 pence = 1 pound

1987

547	10p *Suillus luteus*			
548	24p *Mycena sp*			
549	29p *Camarophyllus adonis*			
	(*Hygrophorus adonis*)			
550	58p *Gerronema schusteri*			
		Set of 4	3·25	3·25

FIJI

South Pacific
100 cents = 1 dollar

1984

670   8c *Dacryopinax spathularia*
671   15c *Podoscypha involuta*
672   40c *Lentinus squarrosulus*
673   50c *Scleroderma flavidum*
674   $1 *Phillipsia domingensis*

Set of 5   3·50   2·75

FINLAND

Northern Europe
100 pennia = 1 markka

1974

859   35p + 5p *Gyromitra esculenta*
860   50p + 10p *Cantharellus cibarius*
861   60p + 15p *Boletus edulis*

Set of 3   2·25   1·75

1978

937   50p + 10p *Lactarius deterrimus*
938   80p + 15p *Macrolepiota procera*
        (*Lepiota procera*)
939   1m + 20p *Rozites caperata*

Set of 3   2·00   1·50

1980

967   60p + 10p *Lactarius torminosus*
968   90p + 15p *Leccinum versipelle*
969   1m10 + 20p *Russula paludosa*

Set of 3   1·75   1·25

FRANCE

Western Europe
100 centimes = 1 franc

1979

2299   64c *Amanita caesarea*
2300   83c *Craterellus cornucopioides*
2301   1f30 *Pleurotus olearius* (*Omphalotus
          olearius*)
2302   2f25 *Ramaria botrytis*

Set of 4   3·25   2·00

Nos. 2299/302 were only issued pre-cancelled. The mint price is for stamps with gum, the used for those without gum.

1987

2786   2f *Gyroporus cyanescens*
2787   3f *Gomphus clavatus*
2788   4f *Morchella conica* (*Morchella
          esculenta*)
2789   5f *Russula virescens*

Set of 4   3·00   90

GABON
West Africa
100 centimes = 1 franc

1978

677 90f Sir Alexander Fleming, chemical formula and laboratory equipment   65   35

GAMBIA
West Africa
100 bututs = 1 dalasy

1982

485† 20b *Stereum ostrea* with *Hylarana galamensis* (frog)   30   10

GERMANY

Central Europe, divided from 1945 until 1990 into West Germany, West Berlin and East Germany.

West Germany
100 pfennige = 1 deutschmark

1980

1945 40pf "Landscape with Two Fir Trees" (etching, A. Altdorfer) (tree stump appears to show bracket fungi)   20   10

East Germany
100 pfennige = 1 mark

1971

E1394† 40pf "The Three Peasants" (Durer) (one carrying a basket of mushrooms)   10   10

1974

E1650 5pf *Rhodophyllus sinuatus* (*Entoloma sinuata*)
E1651 10pf *Boletus satanas*
E1652 15pf *Amanita pantherina*
E1653 20pf *Amanita muscaria*
E1654 25pf *Gyromitra esculenta*
E1655 30pf *Inocybe patouillardii*
E1656 35pf *Amanita phalloides*
E1657 40pf *Clitocybe dealbata*
     Set of 8   3·25   1·60

1980

E2267 5pf *Leccinum versipelle*
E2268 10pf *Boletus erythropus*
E2269 15pf *Agaricus campestris*
E2270 20pf *Boletus badius* (*Xerocomus badius*)
E2271 35pf *Boletus edulis*
E2272 70pf *Cantharellus cibarius*
     Set of 6   2·25   1·75

GREAT BRITAIN

North-west Europe
1967 12 pence = 1 shilling
20 shillings = 1 pound
1971 100 pence = 1 pound

1967

753† 1s *Penicillium notatum*   10   10

1977

1039† 9p *Clitocybe nebularis*? and West
European Hedgehog   25   20

1988

1383† 34p *Morchella esculenta* . . . .   1·10   1·10

GRENADA
West Indies
100 cents = 1 dollar

1986

1521 10c *Lepiota roseolamellata*
1522 60c *Lentinus bertieri*
1523 $1 *Lentinus retinervis*
1524 $4 *Eccilia cystiophorus* (but possibly
       Entoloma cystidiophorum)
                              Set of 4   4·50   4·00
MS1525 $5 *Cystolepiota eriophora* . . .   5·00   5·00

1989

2031 15c *Hygrocybe occidentalis*
2032 40c *Marasmius haematocephalus*
2033 50c *Hygrocybe hypohaemacta*
2034 70c *Lepiota pseudoignicolor*
2035 90c *Cookeina tricholoma*
2036 $1.10 *Leucopaxillus gracillimus*
2037 $2.25 *Hygrocybe nigrescens*
2038 $4 *Clathrus crispus*
                              Set of 8   6·50   6·00
MS2039 Two sheets (a) $6 *Mycena
       holoporphyra*; (b) $6 *Xeromphalina
       tenuipes*
                          Set of 2 sheets   7·50   8·00

GRENADINES OF GRENADA
West Indies
100 cents = 1 dollar

1986

766 15c *Hygrocybe firma*
767 50c *Xerocomus coccolobae*
768 $2 *Volvariella cubensis*
769 $3 *Lactarius putidus*
                              Set of 4   6·00   4·00
MS770 $5 *Leptonia caeruleocapitata* . .   5·00   5·00

1989

GRENADA
GRENADINES   6c

1163 6c *Agaricus purpurellus* (incorrectly
      inscr *Collybia aurea*)
1164 10c *Podaxis pistillaris*
1165 20c *Hygrocybe firma*
1166 30c *Agaricus rufoaurantiacus*
1167 75c *Leptonia howellii*
1168 $2 *Marasmiellus purpureus*
1169 $3 *Marasmius trinitatis*
1170 $4 *Collybia aurea* (incorrectly inscr
      Hygrocybe martinicensis)
                        Set of 8   4·50   4·75
MS1171 Two sheets, (a) $6 *Lentinus
crinitus* (incorrectly inscr *Agaricus
purpurellus*); (b) $6 *Hygrocybe
martinicensis* (incorrectly inscr *Lentinus
crinitus*)
                  Set of 2 sheets   5·50   5·75

GRENADINES OF ST. VINCENT
West Indies
100 cents = 1 dollar

1986

Grenadines of
St.VINCENT
                45c

477 45c *Marasmius pallescens*
478 60c *Leucocoprinus fragilissimus*
479 75c *Hygrocybe occidentalis*
480 $3 *Xerocomus hypoxanthus*
                        Set of 4   4·50   3·75

COLLECT MAMMALS ON STAMPS
A Stanley Gibbons thematic catalogue on this
popular subject. Copies available at £7.50 (p.+ p.
£2.75) from: Stanley Gibbons Publications Ltd,
5 Parkside, Christchurch Road, Ringwood, Hants
BH24 3SH.

GUINEA
West Africa
100 caury = 1 syli

1977

5s

République de Guinée

912 5s *Collybia fusipes*
913 7s *Lycoperdon perlatum*
914 9s *Boletus edulis*
915 9s50 *Lactarius deliciosus*
916 11s50 *Agaricus campestris*
917 10s *Morchella esculenta* (air)
918 12s *Lepiota procera*
919 15s *Cantharellus cibarius*
                        Set of 8   10·00   2·75

1985

5s
REPUBLIQUE DE GUINÉE

1157 5s *Rhodophyllus callidermus*
1158 7s *Agaricus niger*
1159 10s *Termitomyces globulus*
1160 15s *Amanita robusta*
1161 20s *Lepiota subradicans* (air)
1162 25s *Cantharellus rhodophyllus*
                        Set of 6   6·00   3·25
MS1163 30s *Phlebopus silvaticus*
        (*Phaeogyroporus silvaticus*) . . . . . .   2·50   1·75

                    Nos. 1157/63 surcharged
1205 1s on 5s *Rhodophyllus callidermus*
1206 2s on 7s *Agaricus niger*
1207 8s on 10s *Termitomyces globulus*
1208 30s on 15s *Amanita robusta*
1209 35s on 20s *Lepiota subradicans* (air)
1210 40s on 25s *Cantharellus rhodophyllus*
                        Set of 6   8·25   3·75
MS1211 50s on 30s *Phlebopus silvaticus*
        (*Phaeogyroporus silvaticus*) . . . . . .   4·00   1·50

GUINEA – BISSAU
West Africa
100 centavos = 1 peso

1985

924 7p *Clitocybe gibba* (*Clitocybe infundibuliformis*)
925 9p *Morchella elata*
926 12p *Lepista nuda*
927 20p *Lactarius deliciosus*
928 30p *Russula virescens*
929 35p *Chroogomphus rutilus*
                                 Set of 6   1·25   40

HUNGARY
Central Europe
100 filler = 1 forint

1984

3583 1fo *Boletus edulis*
3584 1fo *Marasmius oreades*
3585 2fo *Morchella esculenta*
3586 2fo *Agaricus campestris*
3587 3fo *Cantharellus cibarius*
3588 3fo *Macrolepiota procera* (*Lepiota procera*)
3589 4fo *Armillariella* (*Armillaria*) *mellea*
                                 Set of 7   4·00   1·50

1986

3751 2fo *Amanita phalloides*
3752 2fo *Amanita muscaria*
3753 2fo *Inocybe patouillardii*
3754 4fo *Omphalotus olearius*
3755 4fo *Amanita pantherina*
3756 6fo *Gyromitra esculenta*
                                 Set of 6   5·50   2·75

ITALY
Southern Europe
100 centesimi = 1 lira

1984

1836† 450li Wildlife and building construction (fungi in foreground)   60   30

JAPAN
Eastern Asia
100 sen = 1 yen

1948

483 5y Distillery towers and stylized yeast cells (*Saccharomyces* sp) . . . .   3·75   2·25

1974

1371 20y *Lentinus edodes* 40 5

KAMPUCHEA

South-east Asia
100 cents = 1 riel

1985

606 20c *Gymnopilus spectabilis* var.
      junonia (*Gymnopilus junonius*)
607 50c *Coprinus micaceus*
608 80c *Amanita pantherina*
609 1r *Hebeloma crustuliniforme*
610 1r50 *Amanita muscaria*
611 2r *Coprinus comatus*
612 3r *Amanita caesarea*
                    Set of 7 3·75 1·25

KENYA

East Africa
100 cents = 1 shilling

1984

328† 10s Kenyan products including
      mushrooms . . . . 2·00 2·50

1989

506 1s20 *Pleurotus sajor-caju* (*Lentinus*
      sajor-caju)
507 3s40 *Agaricus bisporus*
508 4s40 *Agaricus bisporus* (different)
509 5s50 *Termitomyces schimperi*
510 7s70 *Lentinus edodes*
                    Set of 5 2·00 2·00

KOREA

Eastern Asia

South Korea

100 chon = 1 won

1969

833† 7w "Agriculture and Fisheries"
      (includes stylized mushrooms) 40 15

North Korea

100 chon = 1 won

1968

N861 5ch *Tricholoma matsutake*
N862 10ch *Lentinus edodes*
N863 10ch *Agaricus bisporus*
                    Set of 3 7·00 85

APPENDIX

The following stamps have either been issued in excess of postal needs, or have not been made available to the public in reasonable quantities at face value. Miniature sheets, imperforate stamps etc. are excluded from this section.

1985

Fungi. 10ch *Pleurotus cornucopiae,* 20ch *Pleurotus ostreatus,* 30ch *Catathelasma ventricosum.*

1986

Minerals and Fungi. 10ch *Clitocybe infundibuliformis,* 15ch *Morchella esculenta.* Air 50ch *Russula cyanoxantha* (three other stamps with the same face values show   minerals)

KUWAIT

Arabian Peninsula
1000 fils = 1 dinar

1983

976†	40f *Montagnites (Montagnea)*		
	candollei	40	30
977†	40f *Terfezia leonis*	40	30

A 15f (No. 958) from this series may depict *Cordyceps militaris,* but is more likely to be the parasitic plant *Cynomorium coccineum.*

LAOS

South-east Asia
100 cents = 1 kip

1985

814	50c *Amanita muscaria*		
815	1k *Boletus edulis*		
816	2k *Coprinus comatus*		
817	2k *Amanita rubescens*		
818	3k *Xerocomus subtomentosus*		
819	4k *Lepiota procera*		
820	8k *Paxillus involutus*		
	Set of 7	65	20

LESOTHO

Southern Africa
100 lisente = 1 maloti

1983

532	10s *Lepista caffrorum*		
533	30s *Broomeia congregata*		
534	50s *Afroboletus luteolus*		
535	75s *Lentinus tuber-regium*		
	Set of 4	1·75	1·50

1989

900	12s *Paxillus involutus*		
901	16s *Ganoderma applanatum*		
902	55s *Suillus granulatus*		
903	5m *Stereum hirsutum*		
	Set of 4	3·00	3·00
MS904	4m *Scleroderma flavidum* . . .	2·50	2·50

LIBERIA
West Africa
100 cents = 1 dollar

1985

Liberia 25c

1619 25c Transplanting rice, with
mushrooms and other produce
1620 31c Transplanting rice, with
mushrooms and other produce
Set of 2 1·00 65

1988

1684 10c Green Revolution (mushrooms in
top panel)
1685 35c Green Revolution (mushrooms in
top panel)
Set of 2 50 35

LIBYA
North Africa
1000 dirhams = 1 dinar

1985

1722 50dh Leucopaxillus lepistoides
1723 50dh Amanita caesarea
1724 50dh Coriolus hirsutus
1725 50dh Cortinarius subfulgens
1726 50dh Dermocybe pratensis
1727 50dh Macrolepiota excoriata
(Leucoagaricus excoriatus)

1728 50dh Amanita curtipes
1729 50dh Trametes ljubarskyi
1730 50dh Pholiota aurivella
1731 50dh Boletus edulis
1732 50dh Geastrum sessile
1733 50dh Russula sanguinea
1734 50dh Cortinarius herculeus
1735 50dh Pholiota lenta
1736 50dh Amanita rubescens
1737 50dh Scleroderma polyrhizum
Set of 16 4·50 2·50

MALAWI
Central Africa
100 tambalas = 1 kwacha

1985

720 7t Leucopaxillus gracillimus
721 20t Limacella guttata
722 30t Termitomyces eurrhizus
723 1k Xerulina asprata (Cyptotrama
asprata)
Set of 4 3·50 2·50

MALDIVE ISLANDS
Indian Ocean
100 larees = 1 rupee

1986

1217 15la Hypholoma fasciculare
1218 50la Kuehneromyces mutabilis
(Galerina mutabilis)
1219 1r Amanita muscaria
1220 2r Agaricus campestris
1221 3r Amanita pantherina
1222 4r Coprinus comatus
1223 5r Pholiota spectabilis (Gymnopilus
junonius)
1224 10r Pluteus cervinus
Set of 8 6·50 6·50
MS1225 Two sheets (a) 15r Armillaria
mellea; (b) 15r Stropharia aeruginosa
Set of 2 sheets 6·00 8·00

MALI
West Africa
100 centimes = 1 franc

1985

1065	120f *Clitocybe nebularis*
1066	200f *Lepiota cortinarius*
1067	485f *Agaricus semotus*
1068	525f *Lepiota procera*

Set of 4   6·00   4·25

MAURITANIA
West Africa
100 cents = 1 ouguiya (um)

1979

606†   12u "Market Peasant and Wife"
(Durer) (with basket of mushrooms)   35   25

MAURITIUS
Indian Ocean
100 cents = 1 rupee

1978

552	20c Problem of infection, World War I
553	1r Microscope and first mould growth, 1928
554	1r50 Mould *Penicillium notatum*
555	5r Sir Alexander Fleming and nurse administering injection

Set of 4   2·50   1·40

MEXICO
North America
100 centavos = 1 peso

1988

1914†   300p *Ustilago maydis*   15   10

MONACO
Southern Europe
100 centimes = 1 franc

1974

1117   45c Ernest Duchesne and *Penicillium*
glaucum   25   10

1988

1888	2f *Leccinum rotundifoliae*
1889	2f20 *Hygrocybe punicea*
1890	2f50 *Pholiota flammans*

1891   2f70 *Lactarius lignyotus*
1892   3f *Cortinarius traganus*
1893   7f *Russula olivacea*

Set of 6   4·00   2·75

MONGOLIA
Central Asia
100 mung = 1 tugrik

196~

327   5m *Coprinus comatus*
328   10m *Lactarius torminosus*
329   15m *Psalliota campestris (Agaricus campestris)*
330   20m *Russula delica*
331   30m *Ixocomus granulatus (Suillus granulatus)*
332   50m *Lactarius scobiculatus*
333   70m *Lactarius deliciosus*
334   1t *Ixocomus variegatus (Suillus variegatus)*

Set of 8   5·00   1·50

1978

1114   20m *Boletus variegatus (Suillus variegatus)*
1115   30m *Russula cyanoxantha*
1116   40m *Boletus aurantiacus (Leccinum aurantiacum)* (but probably *Leccinum versipelle*)
1117   50m *Boletus scaber (Leccinum scabrum)*
1118   60m *Russula flava (Russula claroflava)*
1119   80m *Lactarius resimus*
1120   1t20 *Flammula spumosa (Pholiota spumosa)*

Set of 7   3·50   1·25

MOZAMBIQUE
South-east Africa
100 centavos = 1 metical

1986

1120   4m *Amanita muscaria*
1121   8m *Lactarius deliciosus*
1122   16m *Amanita phalloides*
1123   30m *Tricholoma nudum (Lepista nuda)*

Set of 4   3·00   1·90

NEVIS
West Indies
100 cents = 1 dollar

1987

485   15c *Panaeolus antillarum*
486   50c *Pycnoporus sanguineus*
487   $2 *Gymnopilus chrysopellus*
488   $3 *Cantharellus cinnabarinus*

Set of 4   2·75   2·50

COLLECT MAMMALS ON STAMPS
A Stanley Gibbons thematic catalogue on this popular subject. Copies available at £7.50 (p.+ p. £2.75) from: Stanley Gibbons Publications Ltd, 5 Parkside, Christchurch Road, Ringwood, Hants BH24 3SH.

NEW ZEALAND

Australasia
100 cents = 1 dollar

1988

1463†   40c Brown Kiwi with *Marasmius*? or
        Crinipellis? sp   25   30

NICARAGUA

Central America
100 centavos = 1 cordoba

1985

2648   50c *Strobilomyces retisporus* ?
2649   50c *Boletus calopus* ?
2650   1cor *Boletus luridus* ?

2651   1cor *Xerocomus illudens* ? (air)
2652   4cor *Gyrodon merulioides* ?
2653   5cor *Tylopilus plumbeoviolaceus* ?
2654   8cor *Gyroporus castaneus* ?
                    Set of 7   1·25   50
Inscriptions appear to bear little relationship to the species
illustrated.

NIGER

West Africa
100 centimes = 1 franc

1981

864   150f Sir Alexander Fleming and
      Penicillin   85   35

1985

1044†   150f *Tolyposporium ehrenbergii* and
        Sclerospora graminicola   . . .   80   50

1059   85f *Boletus* sp (possibly *Boletus*
       edulis)
1060   110f *Hypholoma fasciculare*
1061   200f *Coprinus comatus*
1062   300f *Agaricus arvensis*
1063   400f *Geastrum fimbriatum* (*Geastrum*
       sessile)
                    Set of 5   5·50   3·25

NORFOLK ISLAND

Australasia
100 cents = 1 dollar

1983

300	27c	*Panaeolus papilionaceus*
301	40c	*Coprinus domesticus*
302	55c	*Marasmius niveus*
303	65c	*Cymatoderma elegans* var. *lamellata*

Set of 4   2·25   2·25

NORWAY

Northern Europe
100 ore = 1 krone

1987

1004   2k70   *Cantharellus tubaeformis*
      (*Cantharellus infundibuliformis*)
1005   2k70   *Rozites caperata*

Set of 2   1·00   30

1988

1040   2k90   *Lepista nuda*
1041   2k90   *Lactarius deterrimus*

Set of 2   1·25   40

1989

1052   3k   *Cantharellus cibarius*
1053   3k   *Suillus luteus*

Set of 2   1·00   40

PALAU

North Pacific
100 cents = 1 dollar

1989

252   45c   "Gilled Auricularia"
      (*Hygrophoropsis aurantiaca* ?)
253   45c   "Rock Mushroom" (?)
254   45c   "Polyporus" (?)
255   45c   *Phallus indusiatus*

Set of 4   2·00   1·60

PARAGUAY

South America
100 centimos = 1 guarani

APPENDIX

The following stamps have either been issued in excess of postal needs, or have not been made available to the public in reasonable quantities at face value. Miniature sheets, imperforate stamps etc. are excluded from this section.

1985

Fungi. 25c *Boletus luteus* (*Suillus luteus*), 50c *Agaricus campestris*, 1g *Pholiota spectabilis* (*Gymnopilus junonius*), 2g *Tricholoma terreum*, 3g *Laccaria laccata*, 4g *Amanita phalloides*, 5g *Scleroderma verrucosum*.

1986

Fungi. 25c *Lepiota procera*, 50c *Tricholoma albobrunneum*, 1g *Clavaria* sp, 2g *Volvaria* sp, 3g *Lycoperdon perlatum*, 4g *Dictyophora duplicata* (*Phallus duplicatus*), 5g *Polyporus rubrum* ?.

PHILIPPINES

South-east Asia
100 sentimos = 1 piso

1988

2109   60s *Lentinus edodes*
2110   1p *Auricularia polytricha*
2111   2p *Pleurotus sajor-caju* (*Lentinus
        sajor-caju*)
2112   4p *Volvariella volvacea*
                                Set of 4   70   30

POLAND

Eastern Europe
100 groszy = 1 zloty

1959

1087   20g *Amanita phalloides*
1088   30g *Boletus luteus* (*Suillus luteus*)
1089   40g *Boletus edulis*
1090   60g *Lactarius deliciosus*
1091   1z *Cantharellus cibarius*
1092   2z50 *Psalliota campestris* (*Agaricus
        campestris*)
1093   3z40 *Amanita muscaria*
1094   5z60 *Boletus scaber* (*Leccinum
        scabrum*)
                                Set of 8   11·00   2·50

1980

2679   2z *Clathrus ruber*
2680   2z *Scleroderma citrinum* parasitized
        by *Xerocomus parasiticus*
2681   2z50 *Strobilomyces floccopus*
2682   2z50 *Phallus hadriani*
2683   8z *Sparassis crispa*
2684   10z50 *Langermannia gigantea*
                                Set of 6   2·50   60 v

RUMANIA

South-east Europe
100 bani = 1 leu

1958

2583   5b *Lepiota procera*
2584   10b *Clavaria aurea* (*Ramaria aurea*)
2585   20b *Amanita caesarea*
2586   30b *Lactarius deliciosus*
2587   35b *Armillaria mellea*
2588   55b *Coprinus comatus*
2589   1le *Morchella conica* (*Morchella
        esculenta*)
2590   1le55 *Psalliota campestris* (*Agaricus
        campestris*)
2591   1le75 *Boletus edulis*
2592   2le *Cantharellus cibarius*
                                Set of 10   12·00   1·40

1986

5065   50b *Amanita rubescens*
5066   1le *Boletus luridus*
5067   2le *Lactarius piperatus*
5068   3le *Lepiota clypeolaria*
5069   4le *Russula cyanoxantha*
5070   5le *Tremiscus helvelloides* (*Phlogiotis
        helvelloides*)
                                Set of 6   5·00   1·50

RUSSIA

Eastern Europe and Northern Asia
100 kopeks = 1 rouble

1964

3058	2k Suillus luteus		
3059	4k Cantharellus cibarius		
3060	6k Boletus edulis		
3061	10k Leccinum aurantiacum		
3062	12k Lactarius deliciosus		
	Set of 5	2·75	45

1975

4407	6k Cordyceps militaris at bottom right	20	10

1986

5651	4k Amanita phalloides		
5652	5k Amanita muscaria		
5653	10k Amanita pantherina		
5654	15k Tylopilus felleus		
5655	20k Hypholoma fasciculare		
	Set of 5	1·75	50

GIBBONS STAMP MONTHLY

finest and most informative magazine for all
collectors. Obtainable from your newsagents or
by postal subscription — details on request.

RWANDA

Central Africa
100 centimes = 1 franc

1980

988	20c Geastrum sp		
989	30c Lentinus atrobrunneus		
990	50c Gomphus stereoides		
991	4f Cantharellus cibarius		
992	10f Stilbothamnium dybowskii var.		
	laevispora (Aspergillus dybowskii		
	var. laevispora)		
993	15f Xeromphalina tenuipes		
994	70f Podoscypha elegans		
995	100f Mycena sp		
	Set of 8	7·50	2·75

ST. HELENA

South Atlantic
100 pence = 1 pound

1983

415	11p Coriolus versicolor		
416	15p Pluteus brunneisucus		
417	29p Polyporus induratus		
418	59p Coprinus angulatus		
	Set of 4	2·10	2·10

ST. KITTS
West Indies
100 cents = 1 dollar

1987

St.Kitts   15ᶜ

241 15c *Hygrocybe occidentalis*
242 40c *Marasmius haematocephalus*
243 $1.20 *Psilocybe cubensis*
244 $2 *Hygrocybe acutoconica*
245 $3 *Boletellus cubensis*

Set of 5   4·00   4·00

ST. LUCIA
West Indies
100 cents = 1 dollar

1989

1022 15c *Gerronema citrinum*
1023 25c *Lepiota spiculata*
1024 50c *Calocybe cyanocephala*
1025 $5 *Russula puiggarii*

Set of 4   4·00   4·00

ST. PIERRE ET MIQUELON
North Atlantic
100 centimes = 1 franc

1987

587 2f50 *Hygrophorus pratensis*   60   35

1988

598 2f50 *Russula paludosa*   55   35

1989

609 2f50 *Tricholoma virgatum*   50   40

1990

635 2f50 *Hydnum repandum*   50   40

SAMOA
South Pacific
100 sene = 1 tala

1985

696 48s *Dictyophora indusiata* (*Phallus indusiatus*)
697 56s *Ganoderma tornatum*

698 67s *Mycena chlorophos*
699 $1 *Mycobonia flava*
                    Set of 4   1·75   1·75

SAN MARINO
Southern Europe
100 centesimi = 1 lira

1967

826 5li *Amanita caesarea*
827 15li *Clitopilus prunulus*
828 20li *Lepiota procera*
829 40li *Boletus edulis*
830 50li *Russula paludosa*
831 170li *Lyophyllum georgii (Tricholoma*
      gambosum)
                    Set of 6   50   25

SENEGAL
West Africa
100 centimes = 1 franc

1982

749† 80f *Tolyposporium penicillariae* and
      Sclerospora graminicola   60   35

SIERRA LEONE
West Africa
100 cents = 1 leone

1988

1121 3le *Russula cyanoxantha*
1122 10le *Lycoperdon perlatum*
1123 20le *Lactarius deliciosus*
1124 30le *Boletus edulis*
                    Set of 4   2·50   2·50
MS1125 65le *Amanita muscaria* . . . .   1·90   2·00

SOLOMON ISLANDS
West Pacific
100 cents = 1 dollar

1984

513 6c *Calvatia gardneri*
514 18c *Marasmiellus inoderma*
515 35c *Pycnoporus sanguineus*
516 $2 *Filoboletus manipularis*
                    Set of 4   2·50 √3·00

SWAZILAND
Southern Africa
100 cents = 1 emalangeni

1984

462 10c *Suillus bovinus*
463 15c *Langermannia gigantea*
464 50c *Coriolus versicolor*
465 1e *Boletus edulis*
                    Set of 4   2·25   1·40

COLLECT SHIPS ON STAMPS
The largest Stanley Gibbons thematic catalogue
to date — available at £10.50 (p.+ p. £2.75) from:
Stanley Gibbons Publications Ltd, 5 Parkside,
Christchurch Road, Ringwood, Hants BH24 3SH.

SWEDEN

Northern Europe
100 ore = 1 krone

1978

976   1k15 *Russula decolorans*
977   1k15 *Lycoperdon perlatum*
978   1k15 *Macrolepiota procera* (*Lepiota procera*)
979   1k15 *Cantharellus cibarius*
980   1k15 *Boletus edulis*
981   1k15 *Ramaria botrytis*

Set of 6   2·75   2·25

TAIWAN

See under China

THAILAND

South-east Asia
100 satangs = 1 baht

1986

1265   2b *Volvariella volvacea*
1266   2b *Pleurotus ostreatus*
1267   6b *Auricularia polytricha*
1268   6b *Pleurotus cystidiosus*

Set of 4   2·00   65

COLLECT RAILWAYS ON STAMPS

Second revised edition of this Stanley Gibbons thematic catalogue. Copies available at £9.50 (p.+p. £2.75) from: Stanley Gibbons Publications Ltd, 5 Parkside, Christchurch Road, Ringwood, Hants BH24 3SH.

TOGO

West Africa
100 centimes = 1 franc

1986

1893   70f *Ramaria moelleriana*
1894   90f *Hygrocybe firma*
1895   150f *Kalchbrennera corallocephala* (*Lysurus corallocephalus*)
1896   200f *Cookeina tricholoma*

Set of 4   3·50   2·25

TRINIDAD AND TOBAGO

West Indies
100 cents = 1 dollar

1990

770   10c *Xeromphalina tenuipes*
771   40c *Dictyophora indusiata* (*Phallus indusiatus*)
772   $1 *Leucocoprinus birnbaumii*
773   $2.25 *Crinipellis perniciosus*

Set of 4   1·00   1·10

TRISTAN DA CUNHA

South Atlantic
100 pence = 1 pound

1984

369   10p *Agrocybe praecox* var. *cutefracta*
370   20p *Laccaria tetraspora*

371 30p *Agrocybe cylindracea*
372 50p *Sarcoscypha coccinea*
              Set of 4 2·00 2·00

TUVALU

Central Pacific
100 cents = 1 dollar

1988

TUVALU 40c

530 40c *Ganoderma applanatum*
531 50c *Pseudoepicoccum cocos*
532 60c *Rigidoporus zonalis*
533 90c *Rigidoporus microporus*
              Set of 4 3·50 3·00

1989

TUVALU 40c

554 40c *Trametes muelleri*
555 50c *Pestalotiopsis palmarum*
556 60c *Trametes cingulata*
557 90c *Schizophyllum commune*
              Set of 4 3·50 2·75

UGANDA

East Africa
100 cents = 1 shilling

1989

706 10s *Suillus granulatus*
707 15s *Omphalotus olearius*
708 45s *Oudemansiella radicata*
709 50s *Clitocybe nebularis*
710 60s *Macrolepiota rhacodes* (*Lepiota rhacodes*)
711 75s *Lepista nuda*
712 150s *Suillus luteus*
713 200s *Agaricus campestris*
              Set of 8 3·75 4·25
MS714 Two sheets (a) 350s *Bolbitius vitellinus*; (b) 350s *Schizophyllum commune*
            Set of 2 sheets 5·00 5·25

UNITED STATES OF AMERICA

North America
100 cents = 1 dollar

1987

2267† 22c Eastern Chipmunk with *Hypholoma*? sp 35 10
2305† 22c Red Fox with bracket fungi . 35 10

UPPER VOLTA

West Africa
100 centimes = 1 franc

1984

716† 25f *Polystictus leoninus* (*Coltricia leonina*) 10 10
718† 200f *Phlebopus colossus sudanicus* 70 65
720† 300f *Trametes versicolor* (*Coriolus versicolor*) (air) . . . . 1·00 95

721†   400f *Ganoderma lucidum* . . . .   1·40   1·25
MS722   600f *Leucocoprinus cepaestripes,*
Laetiporus sulphureus and Dictyophora
indusiata (Phallus indusiatus) . . . . .   2·00   1·90

VANUATU
South Pacific
Vatus

1984

377   15v *Cymatoderma elegans* var. *lamella*
378   25v *Lignosus rhinoceros*
379   35v *Stereum ostrea*
380   45v *Ganoderma boninense*
                                    Set of 4   2·00   1·75

VIETNAM
South-east Asia

Vietnam Republic
100 xu = 1 dong

1983

628   50x *Pleurotus ostreatus*
629   50x *Coprinus atramentarius*
630   50x *Flammulina velutipes*
631   50x *Cantharellus cibarius*
632   1d *Volvariella volvacea*
633   2d *Agaricus silvaticus*
634   5d *Morchella esculenta*
635   10d *Amanita caesarea*
                            Set of 8   5·50   1·40

1987

1159   5d *Polyporellus squamosus*
          (*Polyporus squamosus*)
1160   10d *Clitocybe geotropa*
1161   15d *Tricholoma terreum*
1162   20d *Russula aurata*
1163   25d *Collybia fusipes*
1164   30d *Cortinarius violaceus*
1165   40d *Boletus aereus*
                            Set of 7   2·50   1·10

WALLIS AND FUTUNA ISLANDS
South Pacific
100 centimes = 1 franc

1980

363   101f Sir Alexander Fleming and
          Penicillin slide . . . .   2·00   1·50

YUGOSLAVIA
South-east Europe
100 paras = 1 dinar

1983

2068   4d *Agaricus campestris*

2069	6d10	*Morchella vulgaris*		
2070	8d80	*Boletus edulis*		
2071	15d	*Cantharellus cibarius*		
		Set of 4	1·40	55

420	12n	*Amanita flammeola*		
421	28n	*Amanita zambiana*		
422	32n	*Termitomyces letestui*		
423	75n	*Cantharellus miniatescens*		
		Set of 4	3·00	2·50

ZAIRE

Central Africa
100 sengi = 1 kuta,
100 kuta = 1 zaire

1979

Phylloporus ampliporus

944	30s	*Phylloporus ampliporus*		
945	5k	*Engleromyces goetzei*		
946	8k	*Scutellinia virungae*		
947	10k	*Pycnoporus sanguineus*		
948	30k	*Cantharellus miniatescens*		
949	40k	*Lactarius phlebonemus*		
950	48k	*Phallus indusiatus*		
951	100k	*Ramaria moelleriana*		
		Set of 8	2·50	1·40

ZAMBIA

Central Africa
100 ngwee = 1 kwacha

1981

342†	12n Mushroom picking		50	25

1984

1985

No. 342 *surcharged* 20n

436†	20n on 12n Mushroom picking	. .	40	15

1989

No. 342 *surcharged* K19.50

585†	19k50 on 12n Mushroom picking	.	1·25	1·40

ZIL ELWANNYEN SESEL

Indian Ocean
100 cents = 1 rupee

1985

95	50c	*Lenzites elegans*		
96	2r	*Xylaria telfairei*		
97	3r	*Lentinus sajor-caju*		
98	10r	*Hexagona tenuis*		
		Set of 4	3·25	3·50

Fungal Species Section

This section contains two parts.

The INDEX contains two alphabetic lists. The first lists fungi by their English name; the second lists them by their systematic (mycological) name. Against each entry is the numerical code for identification in the Systematic Listing.

The second section provides a systematic classification by order and species.

Index

I. By English Name

Abalone Mushroom, *Pleurotus cystidiosus* or *Lentinus sajor-caju* (4-13-8)
Admirable Boletus, *Boletellus mirabilis* (4-13-11)
Agarics The, *Agaricales* (4-13-10)
Agrocybe Mushroom, *Agrocybe cylindracea* (4-13-10)
Antabuse Ink Cap, *Coprinus atramentarius* (4-13-10)
Artist's Fungus, *Ganoderma applanatum* (4-13-8)

Bare-toothed Russula, *Russula vesca* (4-13-12)
Bay Boletus, *Xerocomus badius* (4-13-11)
Beefsteak Morel, *Gyromitra esculenta* (3-2-28)
Beefsteak Mushrooms, *Termitomyces* spp. (4-13-10)
Bird's Nest Fungi, *Nidulariales* (4-14-5)
Bitter Bolete, *Tylopilus felleus* (4-13-11)
Black Mushroom, *Lentinus edodes* (4-13-8)
Black Trumpet, *Craterellus cornucopioides* (4-13-9)
Blackening Wax Cap, *Hygrocybe nigrescens* (4-13-10)
Blue Cap, *Leptonia caeruleocapitata* (4-13-10)
Blue Leg, *Lepista nuda* (4-13-10)
Blue Russula, *Russula cyanoxantha* (4-13-12)
Bluette, *Lepista nuda* (4-13-10)
Blusher The, *Amanita rubescens* (4-13-10)
Boletes The, *Boletales* (4-13-11)
Boot-lace Fungus, *Armillaria mellea* (4-13-10)
Bracket Fungi, *Aphyllophorales* (4-13-8)
Brain Fungus, *Sparassis crispa* (4-13-8)
Bronze Boletus, *Boletus aereus* (4-13-11)
Brown Birch Bolete, *Leccinum scabrum* (4-13-11)
Brown Cap, *Xeromphalina tenuipes* (4-13-10)
Brown Leaf Spot, *Pseudoepicoccum cocos* (5-18)
Brown Mushroom, *Lentinus edodes* (4-13-8)
Brown Roll-rim, *Paxillus involutus* (4-13-11)
Buff Cap, *Hygrophorus pratensis* (4-13-10)
Butter Mushroom, *Suillus luteus* (4-13-11)

Caesar's Mushroom, *Amanita caesarea* (4-13-10)
Cape Russula, *Russula capensis* (4-13-12)
Cauliflower Clavaria, *Ramaria botrytis* (4-13-8)
Cauliflower Fungus, *Sparassis crispa* (4-13-8)
Cep, *Boletus edulis* (4-13-11)
Changeable Agaric, *Galerina mutabilis* (4-13-10)
Changing Pholiota, *Galerina mutabilis* (4-13-10)

Chanterelle, *Cantharellus cibarius* (4-13-9)
Charcoal Burner The, *Russula cyanoxantha* (4-13-12)
Chestnut Boletus, *Xerocomus badius* or *Gyroporus castaneus* (4-13-11)
Chestnut Mushroom, *Xerocomus badius* (4-13-11)
Chicken Mushroom, *Laetiporus sulphureus* (4-13-8)
Chicken of the Woods, *Laetiporus sulphureus* (4-13-8)
Chinese Mushroom, *Volvariella volvacea* (4-13-10)
Cinnabar Chanterelle, *Cantharellus cinnabarinus* (4-13-9)
Clouded Agaric, *Clitocybe nebularis* (4-13-10)
Clouded Clitocybe, *Clitocybe nebularis* (4-13-10)
Clover Windling, *Marasmius oreades* (4-13-10)
Clustered Woodlover, *Hypholoma fasciculare* (4-13-10)
Common Bird's Nest, *Crucibulum laeve* (4-14-5)
Common Earth-ball *Scleroderma citrinum* (4-14-1)
Common Fawn Agaric, *Pluteus cervinus* (4-13-10)
Common Funnel Cap, *Clitocybe infundibuliformis* (4-13-10)
Common Ganoderma, *Ganoderma applanatum* (4-13-8)
Common Ink Cap, *Coprinus atramentarius* (4-13-10)
Common Morel, *Morchella esculenta* or *M. vulgaris* (3-2-28)
Common Puff-ball, *Lycoperdon perlatum* (4-14-4)
Cone-like Boletus, *Strobilomyces floccopus* (4-13-11)
Cow Boletus, *Suillus bovinus* (4-13-11)
Cow Fungus, *Leccinum scabrum* (4-13-11)
Cracked Green Russula, *Russula virescens* (4-13-12)
Crimson Wax Cap, *Hygrocybe punicea* (4-13-10)
Cultivated Mushroom, *Agaricus bisporus* (4-13-10)

Deadly Amanite, *Amanita phalloides* (4-13-10)
Death Cap, *Amanita phalloides* (4-13-10)
Death Trumpet, *Craterellus cornucopioides* (4-13-9)
Deer Mushroom, *Pluteus cervinus* (4-13-10)
Destroying Angel, *Amanita virosa* (4-13-10)
Devil's Boletus, *Boletus satanas* (4-13-11)
Devil's Tobacco Pouch, *Lycoperdon perlatum* (4-14-4)
Downy Boletus, *Xerocomus subtomentosus* (4-13-11)
Dryad's Saddle, *Polyporus squamosus* (4-13-8)

Ear Mushroom, *Auricularia polytricha* (4-13-2)
Earth-balls The, *Sclerodermatales* (4-14-1)
Edible Morel, *Morchella esculenta* (3-2-28)
Edible Mushroom, *Boletus edulis* (4-13-11)
Elegant Boletus, *Suillus grevillei* (4-13-11)
Elephant's Ears, *Gyromitra esculenta* (3-2-28)

Fairy Cake Hebeloma, *Hebeloma crustuliniforme* (4-13-10)
Fairy Cake Mushroom, *Hebeloma crustuliniforme* (4-13-10)
Fairy Ring Champignon, *Marasmius oreades* (4-13-10)
False Blusher, *Amanita pantherina* (4-13-10)
False Chanterelle, *Hygrophoropsis aurantiaca* (4-13-11) sometimes *Omphalotus olearius* (4-13-10)
False Death Cap, *Amanita citrina* (4-13-10)
False Morel, *Gyromitra esculenta* (3-2-28)
False Parasol, *Chlorophyllum molybdites* (4-13-10)
False Turkey Tail, *Stereum ostrea* (4-13-8)
Field Mushroom, *Agaricus campestris* (4-13-10)
Flaky-stemmed Witches' Mushroom, *Boletus erythropus* (4-13-11)
Fly Agaric, *Amanita muscaria* (4-13-10)
Funnel-shaped Chanterelle, *Cantharellus infundibuliformis* (4-13-9)

Vermilion Chanterelle, *Cantharellus cinnabarinus* (4-13-9)

Warted Agaric, *Amanita pantherina* (4-13-10)
White Button Mushroom, *Agaricus bisporus* (4-13-10)
White Jelly Fungus, *Tremella fuciformis* (4-13-1)
White Oyster Mushroom, *Pleurotus ostreatus* (4-13-8)
White Parasol Mushroom, *Macrolepiota zeyheri* (4-13-10)
Winter Fungus, *Flammulina velutipes* (4-13-10)
Witches' Broom of Cacao, *Crinipellis perniciosus* (4-13-10)
Wood Blewit(s), *Lepista nuda* (4-13-10)
Wood Hedgehog, *Hydnum repandum* (4-13-8)
Wood Mushroom, *Agaricus silvaticus*, also *A. silvicola* (4-13-10)
Wood Rot, *Schizophyllum commune* (4-13-8)
Wood Urchin, *Hydnum repandum* (4-13-8)
Woolly Milk Cap, *Lactarius torminosus* (4-13-12)
Wrinkled Pholiota, *Rozites caperata* (4-13-10)

Yeasts, typically *Saccharomycetaceae* (*Endomycetales*) (3-2-11)
Yellow Chanterelle, *Cantharellus cibarius* (4-13-9)
Yellow Cow-pat Toadstool, *Bolbitius vitellinus* (4-13-10)
Yellow Stainer, *Agaricus xanthodermus* (4-13-10)
Yellow Swamp Russula, *Russula claroflava* (4-13-12)
Yellow-brown Boletus, *Suillus luteus* (4-13-11)

II. By Systematic Name

acutoconica, Hygrocybe see 4-13-10 (*Agaricales*)
adonis, Hygrophorus or *Camarophyllus* see 4-13-10 (*Agaricales*)
aegerita, Pholiota = *Agrocybe cylindracea* see 4-13-10 (*Agaricales*)
aereus, Boletus or *Tubiporus* see 4-13-11 (*Boletales*)
aeruginosa, Stropharia see 4-13-10 (*Agaricales*)
africanus, Leucocoprinus see 4-13-10 (*Agaricales*)
Afroboletus see 4-13-11 (*Boletales*)
Agaricus see 4-13-10 (*Agaricales*)
Agrocybe see 4-13-10 (*Agaricales*)
Amanita see 4-13-10 (*Agaricales*)
ampliporus, Phylloporus see 4-13-11 (*Boletales*)
angulatus, Coprinus see 4-13-10 (*Agaricales*)
anthidepas, Trogia see 4-13-10 (*Agaricales*)
antillarum, Panaeolus see 4-13-10 (*Agaricales*)
applanatum, Ganoderma see 4-13-8 (*Aphyllophorales*)
arborescens, Marasmius or *Synpodia* see 4-13-10 (*Agaricales*)
Armillaria or *Armillariella* see 4-13-10 (*Agaricales*)
arvensis, Agaricus see 4-13-10 (*Agaricales*)
Aspergillus see 5-18 (*Hyphomycetes*)
asprata, Cyptotrama or *Xerulina* see 4-13-10 (*Agaricales*)
Astraeus see 4-14-1 (*Sclerodermatales*)
atramentarius, Coprinus see 4-13-10 (*Agaricales*)
atrobrunneus, Lentinus see 4-13-8 (*Aphyllophorales*)
aurantiaca, Hygrophoropsis see 4-13-11 (*Boletales*)
aurantiacum, Leccinum see 4-13-11 (*Boletales*)
aurantiacus, Boletus = *Leccinum aurantiacum* see 4-13-11 (*Boletales*)
aurantiacus, Cantharellus = *Hygrophoropsis aurantiaca* see 4-13-11 (*Boletales*)
aurantiacus, Termitomyces see 4-13-10 (*Agaricales*)
aurantium, Scleroderma = *Scleroderma citrinum* see 4-14-1 (*Sclerodermatales*)
aurata, Russula see 4-13-12 (*Russulales*)
aurea, Clavaria = *Ramaria aurea* see 4-13-8 (*Aphyllophorales*)
aurea, Collybia see 4-13-10 (*Agaricales*)
aurea, Ramaria see 4-13-8 (*Aphyllophorales*)

Auricularia see 4-13-2 (*Auriculariales*)
aurivella, Pholiota see 4-13-10 (*Agaricales*)
austrovenetus, Cortinarius see 4-13-10 (*Agaricales*)

badius, Xerocomus or *Boletus* or *Suillus* see 4-13-11 (*Boletales*)
bertieri, Lentinus see 4-13-8 (*Aphyllophorales*)
birnbaumii, Leucocoprinus see 4-13-10 (*Agaricales*)
bisporus, Agaricus see 4-13-10 (*Agaricales*)
Bolbitius see 4-13-10 (*Agaricales*)
Boletellus see 4-13-11 (*Boletales*)
Boletus see 4-13-11 (*Boletales*)
boninense, Ganoderma see 4-13-8 (*Aphyllophorales*)
botrytis, Ramaria or *Clavaria* see 4-13-8 (*Aphyllophorales*)
boudieri, Terfezia see 3-2-28 (*Pezizales*)
bovinus, Suillus or *Boletus* see 4-13-11 (*Boletales*)
brebissonii, Leucocoprinus or *Lepiota* see 4-13-10 (*Agaricales*)
brevipes, Russula = *Russula delica* see 4-13-12 (*Russulales*)
Broomeia see 4-14-4 (*Lycoperdales*)
brunneisucus, Pluteus see 4-13-10 (*Agaricales*)
brunneoleucum, Hydnum = *Mycobonia flava* see 4-13-8 (*Aphyllophorales*)
buccinalis, Trogia see 4-13-10 (*Agaricales*)

caeruleocapitata, Leptonia see 4-13-10 (*Agaricales*)
caerulescens, Psilocybe see 4-13-10 (*Agaricales*)
caesarea, Amanita see 4-13-10 (*Agaricales*)
caffrorum, Lepista see 4-13-10 (*Agaricales*)
callidermus, Rhodophyllus see 4-13-10 (*Agaricales*)
Calocybe see 4-13-10 (*Agaricales*)
calopus, Boletus see 4-13-11 (*Boletales*)
Calvatia see 4-14-4 (*Lycoperdales*)
Camarophyllus = *Hygrophorus* see 4-13-10 (*Agaricales*)
campestris, Agaricus see 4-13-10 (*Agaricales*)
cancellatus, Clathrus see 4-14-6 (*Phallales*)
candollei, Montagnea or *Montagnites* see 4-14-9 (*Podaxales*)
Cantharellus see 4-13-9 (*Cantharellales*)
capensis, Russula see 4-13-12 (*Russulales*)
caperata, Rozites or *Pholiota* see 4-13-10 (*Agaricales*)
caperatus, Cortinarius = *Rozites caperata* see 4-13-10 (*Agaricales*)
castaneus, Gyroporus or *Boletus* see 4-13-11 (*Boletales*)
cepaestripes, Leucocoprinus see 4-13-10 (*Agaricales*)
cervinus, Pluteus see 4-13-10 (*Agaricales*)
chlorophos, Mycena see 4-13-10 (*Agaricales*)
Chlorophyllum see 4-13-10 (*Agaricales*)
Chroogomphus see 4-13-11 (*Boletales*)
chrysopellus, Gymnopilus see 4-13-10 (*Agaricales*)
cibarius, Cantharellus see 4-13-9 (*Cantharellales*)
cingulata, Trametes see 4-13-8 (*Aphyllophorales*)
cinnabarinus, Cantharellus see 4-13-9 (*Cantharellales*)
cinnabarinus, Cortinarius see 4-13-10 (*Agaricales*)
citrina, Amanita see 4-13-10 (*Agaricales*)
citrinum, Gerronema see 4-13-10 (*Agaricales*)
citrinum, Scleroderma see 4-14-1 (*Sclerodermatales*)
claroflava, Russula see 4-13-12 (*Russulales*)
Clathrus see 4-14-6 (*Phallales*)
Clavariella = *Ramaria* see 4-13-8 (*Apyhllophorales*)
clavatus, Gomphus see 4-13-8 (*Aphyllophorales*)
Clavulinopsis see 4-13-8 (*Aphyllophorales*)
Clitocybe see 4-13-10 (*Agaricales*)
Clitopilus see 4-13-10 (*Agaricales*)
clypeolaria, Lepiota see 4-13-10 (*Agaricales*)
coccinea, Sarcoscypha or *Peziza* see 3-2-28 (*Pezizales*)
coccolobae, Xeromocus see 4-13-11 (*Boletales*)
cocos, Pseudoepicoccum see 5-18 (*Hyphomycetes*)
Collybia see 4-13-10 (*Agaricales*)
colossus, Phlebopus see 4-13-11 (*Boletales*)

haematocephalus, Marasmius see 4-13-10 (*Agaricales*)
Hebeloma see 4-13-10 (*Agaricales*)
helvelloides, Phlogiotis or Tremiscus see 4-13-1 (*Tremellales*)
herculeus, Cortinarius see 4-13-10 (*Agaricales*)
Hericium see 4-13-8 (*Aphyllophorales*)
Hexagona see 4-13-8 (*Aphyllophorales*)
hirsuta, Trametes = Coriolus hirsutus see 4-13-8 (*Aphyllophorales*)
hirsutum, Stereum see 4-13-8 (*Aphyllophorales*)
hirsutus, Coriolus see 4-13-8 (*Aphyllophorales*)
holoporphyra, Mycena see 4-13-10 (*Agaricales*)
howellii, Leptonia see 4-13-10 (*Agaricales*)
Hydnum see 4-13-8 (*Aphyllophorales*)
Hygrocybe see 4-13-10 (*Agaricales*)
hygrometricum, Geastrum = Astraeus hygrometricus see 4-14-1 (*Sclerodermatales*)
hygrometricus, Astraeus see 4-14-1 (*Sclerodermatales*)
Hygrophoropsis see 4-13-11 (*Boletales*)
Hygrophorus see 4-13-10 (*Agaricales*)
Hypholoma see 4-13-10 (*Agaricales*)
hypohaemacta, Hygrocybe see 4-13-10 (*Agaricales*)
hypoxanthus, Xerocomus see 4-13-11 (*Boletales*)

illudens, Clitocybe = Omphalotus olearius see 4-13-10 (*Agaricales*)
illudens, Xerocomus see 4-13-11 (*Boletales*)
imbricata, Macrolepiota see 4-13-10 (*Agaricales*)
induratus, Polyporus see 4-13-8 (*Aphyllophorales*)
indusiata, Dictyophora = Phallus indusiatus 4-14-6 (*Phallales*)
indusiatus, Phallus see 4-14-6 (*Phallales*)
infundibuliformis, Cantharellus see 4-13-9 (*Cantharellales*)
infundibuliformis, Clitocybe see 4-13-10 (*Agaricales*)
Inocybe see 4-13-10 (*Agaricales*)
inoderma, Marasmiellus see 4-13-10 (*Agaricales*)
involuta, Podoscypha see 4-13-8 (*Aphyllophorales*)
involutus, Paxillus see 4-13-11 (*Boletales*)
Ixocomus = Suillus 4-13-11 (*Boletales*)

junonius, Gymnopilus see 4-13-10 (*Agaricales*)

Kalchbrennera = Lysurus 4-14-6 (*Phallales*)
Krombholzia = Leccinum 4-13-11 (*Boletales*)
Kuehneromyces = Galerina see 4-13-10 (*Agaricales*)

Laccaria see 4-13-10 (*Agaricales*)
Lactarius see 4-13-12 (*Russulales*)
Laetiporus see 4-13-8 (*Aphyllophorales*)
laeve, Crucibulum see 4-14-5 (*Nidulariales*)
lancipes, Collybia = Collybia fusipes see 4-13-10 (*Agaricales*)
Langermannia see 4-14-4 (*Lycoperdales*)
Lasiosphaera = Langermannia see 4-14-4 (*Lycoperdales*)
Leccinum see 4-13-11 (*Boletales*)
lenta, Pholiota see 4-13-10 (*Agaricales*)
Lentinus see 4-13-8 (*Aphyllophorales*)
Lenzites see 4-13-8 (*Aphyllophorales*)
leonina, Coltricia see 4-13-8 (*Aphyllophorales*)
leoninus, Polystictus = Coltricia leonina 4-13-8 (*Aphyllophorales*)
leonis, Terfezia see 3-2-28 (*Pezizales*)
Lepiota see 4-13-10 (*Agaricales*)
Lepista see 4-13-10 (*Agaricales*)
lepistoides, Leucopaxillus see 4-13-10 (*Agaricales*)
Leptonia see 4-13-10 (*Agaricales*)
Leptoporus = Tyromyces 4-13-8 (*Aphyllophorales*)
letestui, Termitomyces see 4-13-10 (*Agaricales*)
Leucoagaricus see 4-13-10 (*Agaricales*)
Leucocoprinus see 4-13-10 (*Agaricales*)
Leucopaxillus see 4-13-10 (*Agaricales*)

levis, Pleurotus see 4-13-8 (*Aphyllophorales*)
licmophora, Lepiota = Leucocoprinus fragilissimus see 4-13-10 (*Agaricales*)
Lignosus see 4-13-8 (*Aphyllophorales*)
lignosus, Tyromyces or *Leptoporus* see 4-13-8 (*Aphyllophorales*)
lignyotus, Lactarius see 4-13-12 (*Russulales*)
lilloi, Amanita see 4-13-10 (*Agaricales*)
Limacella see 4-13-10 (*Agaricales*)
ljubarskyi, Trametes see 4-13-8 (*Aphyllophorales*)
lobayensis, Tricholoma see 4-13-10 (*Agaricales*)
longipes, Haddowia see 4-13-8 (*Aphyllophorales*)
lucidum, Ganoderma see 4-13-8 (*Aphyllophorales*)
luridus, Boletus see 4-13-11 (*Boletales*)
luteobubalina, Armillaria see 4-13-10 (*Agaricales*)
luteolus, Afroboletus see 4-13-11 (*Boletales*)
luteus, Suillus or *Boletus* see 4-13-11 (*Boletales*)
Lycoperdon see 4-14-4 (*Lycoperdales*)
Lyophyllum = Tricholoma see 4-13-10 (*Agaricales*)
Lysurus see 4-14-6 (*Phallales*)

Macrolepiota see 4-13-10 (*Agaricales*)
mammiformis, Termitomyces see 4-13-10 (*Agaricales*)
manipularis, Filoboletus see 4-13-10 (*Agaricales*)
Marasmiellus see 4-13-10 (*Agaricales*)
Marasmius see 4-13-10 (*Agaricales*)
marginata, Galerina see 4-13-10 (*Agaricales*)
marginatum, Lycoperdon see 4-14-4 (*Lycoperdales*)
martinicensis, Hygrocybe see 4-13-10 (*Agaricales*)
matsutake, Tricholoma or *Armillaria* see 4-13-10 (*Agaricales*)
maxima, Clitocybe = Clitocybe geotropa see 4-13-10 (*Agaricales*)
maydis, Ustilago see 4-16-1 (*Ustilaginales*)
Melanopus = Polyporus see 4-13-8 (*Aphyllophorales*)
mellea, Armillaria see 4-13-10 (*Agaricales*)
merulioides, Gyrodon see 4-13-11 (*Boletales*)
micaceus, Coprinus see 4-13-10 (*Agaricales*)
microcarpus, Termitomyces see 4-13-10 (*Agaricales*)
Microporus see 4-13-8 (*Aphyllophorales*)
microporus, Rigidoporus see 4-13-8 (*Aphyllophorales*)
militaris, Cordyceps see 3-2-4 (*Clavicipitales*)
miniatescens, Cantharellus see 4-13-9 (*Cantharellales*)
mirabilis, Boletellus or *Boletus* see 4-13-11 (*Boletales*)
moelleriana, Ramaria see 4-13-8 (*Aphyllophorales*)
molybdites, Chlorophyllum see 4-13-10 (*Agaricales*)
Montagnea or *Montagnites* see 4-14-9 (*Podaxales*)
Morchella see 3-2-28 (*Pezizales*)
Mucidula = Oudemansiella see 4-13-10 (*Agaricales*)
mucosus, Cortinarius see 4-13-10 (*Agaricales*)
muelleri, Trametes see 4-13-8 (*Aphyllophorales*)
muscaria, Amanita see 4-13-10 (*Agaricales*)
mutabilis, Galerina or *Kuehneromyces* or *Pholiota* see 4-13-10 (*Agaricales*)
Mycena see 4-13-10 (*Agaricales*)
Mycobonia see 4-13-8 (*Aphyllophorales*)

Naematoloma = Hypholoma see 4-13-10 (*Agaricales*)
nebularis, Clitocybe see 4-13-10 (*Agaricales*)
niger, Agaricus see 4-13-10 (*Agaricales*)
nigrescens, Hygrocybe or *Hygrophorus* see 4-13-10 (*Agaricales*)
niveus, Marasmius see 4-13-10 (*Agaricales*)
Nolanea see 4-13-10 (*Agaricales*)
notatum, Penicillium see 5-18 (*Hyphomycetes*)
nuda, Lepista see 4-13-10 (*Agaricales*)
nudum, Tricholoma = Lepista nuda see 4-13-10 (*Agaricales*)
nudus, Rhodopaxillus = Lepista nuda see 4-13-10 (*Agaricales*)

occidentalis, Hygrocybe or Hygrophorus see 4-13-10 (Agaricales)
olearius, Omphalotus or Pleurotus see 4-13-10 (Agaricales)
olivacea, Russula see 4-13-12 (Russulales)
Omphalotus see 4-13-10 (Agaricales)
oreades, Marasmius see 4-13-10 (Agaricales)
orellanus, Cortinarius see 4-13-10 (Agaricales)
ostrea, Stereum see 4-13-8 (Aphyllophorales)
ostreatus, Pleurotus see 4-13-8 (Aphyllophorales)
Oudemansiella see 4-13-10 (Agaricales)

pachypus, Boletus = Boletus calopus 4-13-11 (Boletales)
pallescens, Marasmius see 4-13-10 (Agaricales)
palmarum, Pestalotiopsis see 5-17 (Coelomycetes)
paludosa, Russula see 4-13-12 (Russulales)
Panaeolus see 4-13-10 (Agaricales)
pantherina, Amanita see 4-13-10 (Agaricales)
papilionaceus, Panaeolus see 4-13-10 (Agaricales)
parasiticus, Xerocomus or Boletus see 4-13-11 (Boletales)
patouillardii, Inocybe see 4-13-10 (Agaricales)
Paxillopsis = Clitopilus see 4-13-10 (Agaricales)
Paxillus see 4-13-11 (Boletales)
penicillariae, Tolyposporium see 4-16-1 (Ustilaginales)
Penicillium see 5-18 (Hyphomycetes)
pergamenus, Lactarius = Lactarius piperatus see 4-13-12 (Russulales)
perlatum, Lycoperdon see 4-14-4 (Lycoperdales)
perniciosus, Crinipellis or Marasmius see 4-13-10 (Agaricales)
Pestalotiopsis see 5-17 (Coelomycetes)
Phaeogyroporus see 4-13-11 (Boletales)
phalloides, Amanita see 4 13-10 (Agaricales)
Phallus see 4-14-6 (Phallales)
Phillipsia see 3-2-28 (Pezizales)
phlebonemus, Lactarius see 4-13-12 (Russulales)
Phlebopus see 4-13-11 (Boletales)
Phlogiotis see 4-13-1 (Tremellales)
Pholiota see 4-13-10 (Agaricales)
Phylloporus see 4-13-11 (Boletales)
piperatus, Lactarius see 4-13-12 (Russulales)
pistillaris, Podaxis see 4-14-9 (Podaxales)
Pleurotus see 4-13-8 (Aphyllophorales)
plumbeoviolaceus, Tylopilus see 4-13-11 (Boletales)
Pluteus see 4-13-10 (Agaricales)
Podaxis see 4-14-9 (Podaxales)
Podoscypha see 4-13-8 (Aphyllophorales)
polymyces, Armillaria = Armillaria mellea see 4-13-10 (Agaricales)
Polyporellus = Polyporus see 4-13-8 (Aphyllophorales)
Polyporus see 4-13-8 (Aphyllophorales)
polyrhizum, Scleroderma see 4-14-1 (Sclerodermatales)
Polystictus = Coltricia see 4-13-8 (Aphyllophorales)
polytricha, Auricularia see 4-13-2 (Auriculariales)
praecox, Agrocybe or Pholiota see 4-13-10 (Agaricales)
pratensis, Camarophyllus = Hygrophorus pratensis see 4-13-10 (Agaricales)
pratensis, Dermocybe see 4-13-10 (Agaricales)
pratensis, Hygrophorus see 4-13-10 (Agaricales)
procera, Lepiota or Macrolepiota see 4-13-10 (Agaricales)
procerus, Leucocoprinus = Lepiota procera see 4-13-10 (Agaricales)
prunulus, Clitopilus or Paxillopsis see 4-13-10 (Agaricales)
Psalliota = Agaricus 4-13-10 (Agaricales)
Psathyrella see 4-13-10 (Agaricales)
pseudoconica, Hygrocybe = Hygrocybe nigrescens see 4-13-10 (Agaricales)
Pseudoepicoccum see 5-18 (Hyphomycetes)
pseudoignicolor, Lepiota see 4-13-10 (Agaricales)
Psilocybe see 4-13-10 (Agaricales)
quiggarii, Russula see 4-13-12 (Russulales)
punicea, Hygrocybe see 4-13-10 (Agaricales)

puniceus, Hygrophorus = Hygrocybe punicea see 4-13-10 (Agaricales)
pura, Mycena see 4-13-10 (Agaricales)
purpurellus, Agaricus see 4-13-10 (Agaricales)
purpureus, Marasmiellus see 4-13-10 (Agaricales)
putidus, Lactarius see 4-13-12 (Russulales)
Pycnoporus see 4-13-8 (Aphyllophorales)
Pyrrhoglossum see 4-13-10 (Agaricales)
pyrrhum, Pyrrhoglossum see 4-13-10 (Agaricales)

radicata, Oudemansiella or Collybia or Mucidula see 4-13-10 (Agaricales)
Ramaria see 4-13-8 (Aphyllophorales)
regius, Boletus see 4-13-11 (Boletales)
repandum, Hydnum see 4-13-8 (Aphyllophorales)
resimus, Lactarius see 4-13-12 (Russulales)
retinervis, Lentinus see 4-13-8 (Aphyllophorales)
retisporus, Strobilomyces see 4-13-11 (Boletales)
rhacodes, Lepiota or Macrolepiota see 4-13-10 (Agaricales)
rhinoceros, Lignosus see 4-13-8 (Aphyllophorales)
Rhodopaxillus = Lepista see 4-13-10 (Agaricales)
Rhodophyllus see 4-13-10 (Agaricales)
rhodophyllus, Cantharellus see 4-13-9 (Cantharellales)
Rigidoporus see 4-13-8 (Aphyllophorales)
rivulosa, Clitocybe = Clitocybe dealbata see 4-13-10 (Agaricales)
robusta, Amanita see 4-13-10 (Agaricales)
robustus, Termitomyces see 4-13-10 (Agaricales)
roseolamellata, Lepiota see 4-13-10 (Agaricales)
rotundifoliae, Leccinum see 4-13-11 (Boletales)
Rozites see 4-13-10 (Agaricales)
ruber, Clathrus see 4-14-6 (Phallales)
rubescens, Amanita see 4-13-10 (Agaricales)
rubra, Russula see 4-13-12 (Russulales)
rufescens, Geastrum = Geastrum sessile see 4-14-4 (Lycoperdales)
rufescens, Krombholzia = Leccinum versipelle see 4-13-11 (Boletales)
rufoaurantiacus, Agaricus see 4-13-10 (Agaricales)
Russula see 4-13-12 (Russulales)
rutilans, Tricholomopsis or Tricholoma see 4-13-10 (Agaricales)
rutilus, Chroogomphus or Gomphidius see 4-13-11 (Boletales)

Saccharomyces see 3-2-11 (Endomycetales)
sajor-caju, Lentinus or Pleurotus see 4-13-8 (Aphyllophorales)
sanguifluus, Lactarius see 4-13-12 (Russulales)
sanguinea, Russula see 4-13-12 (Russulales)
sanguineus, Pycnoporus or Polyporus see 4-13-8 (Aphyllophorales)
Sarcoscypha see 3-2-28 (Pezizales)
satanas, Boletus see 4-13-11 (Boletales)
scaber, Boletus or Trachypus = Leccinum scabrum see 4-13-11 (Boletales)
scabrum, Leccinum see 4-13-11 (Boletales)
schimperi, Termitomyces see 4-13-10 (Agaricales)
Schizophyllum see 4-13-8 (Aphyllophorales)
schusteri, Gerronema see 4-13-10 (Agaricales)
Scleroderma see 4-14-1 (Sclerodermatales)
Sclerospora see 1-10-4 (Peronosporales)
scobiculatus, Lactarius see 4-13-12 (Russulales)
scorodonius, Marasmius see 4-13-10 (Agaricales)
Scutellinia see 3-2-28 (Pezizales)
sebedulis, Agaricus see 4-13-10 (Agaricales)
semotus, Agaricus see 4-13-10 (Agaricales)
sessile, Geastrum see 4-14-4 (Lycoperdales)
silvaticus, Agaricus see 4-13-10 (Agaricales)
silvaticus, Phaeogyroporus or Phlebopus see 4-13-11 (Boletales)

Systematic Listing

The current fungi classification is outlined below. The table provides further details of Genera and Families (ending "-aceae") which make up each Order.

1-10-4 PERONOSPORALES
Peronosporaceae — Sclerospora

3-2-4 CLAVICIPITALES
Clavicipitaceae — Cordyceps

3-2-11 ENDOMYCETALES
Saccharomycetaceae — Saccharomyces

3-2-21 LECANORALES
Cladoniaceae — Cladonia
Parmeliaceae — Evernia, Parmelia, Usnea
Umbilicariaceae — Umbilicaria

3-2-28 PEZIZALES
Humariaceae — Scutellinia
Sarcosomataceae — Cookeina, Phillipsia, Sarcoscypha
Morchellaceae — Gyromitra, Morchella
Terfeziaceae — Terfezia

3-2-34 SPHAERIALES
Xylariaceae — Engleromyces, Xylaria

3-2-36 TELOSCHISTALES
Teloschistaceae — Xanthoria

4-13-1 TREMELLALES
Tremellaceae — Phlogiotis, Tremella

4-13-2 AURICULARIALES
Auriculariaceae — Auricularia

4-13-6 DACRYMYCETALES
Dacrymycetaceae — Dacryopinax

4-13-8 APHYLLOPHORALES
Gomphaceae — Gomphus, Ramaria
Stereaceae — Cymatoderma, Mycobonia, Podoscypha, Stereum
Schizophyllaceae — Schizophyllum
Clavariaceae — Clavulinopsis
Sparassidaceae — Sparassis
Hericiaceae — Hericium
Hydnaceae — Hydnum
Ganodermataceae — Ganoderma, Haddowia
Hymenochaetaceae — Coltricia
Polyporaceae — Coriolus, Hexagona, Laetiporus, Lentinus, Lenzites, Lignosus, Microporus, Pleurotus, Polyporus, Pycnoporus, Rigidoporus, Trametes, Tyromyces

4-13-9 CANTHARELLALES
Cantharellaceae — Cantharellus, Craterellus

4-13-10 AGARICALES
Agaricaceae — Agaricus, Chlorophyllum, Lepiota, Leucocoprinus, Macrolepiota
Amanitaceae — Amanita, Limacella, Termitomyces
Bolbitiaceae — Agrocybe, Bolbitius
Coprinaceae — Coprinus, Psathyrella

Cortinariaceae — Cortinarius, Dermocybe, Galerina, Gymnopilus, Hebeloma, Inocybe, Pyrrhoglossum, Rozites
Entolomataceae — Clitopilus, Eccilia, Entoloma, Leptonia, Nolanea, Rhodophyllus
Hygrophoraceae — Hygrocybe, Hygrophorus
Pluteaceae — Pluteus, Volvariella
Strophariaceae — Hypholoma, Panaeolus, Pholiota, Psilocybe, Stropharia
Tricholomataceae — Armillaria, Calocybe, Clitocybe, Collybia, Crinipellis, Cystolepiota, Filoboletus, Flammulina, Gerronema, Laccaria, Lepista, Leucopaxillus, Marasmiellus, Marasmius, Mycena, Omphalotus, Oudemansiella, Tricholoma, Tricholomopsis, Trogia, Xeromphalina, Xerulina

4-13-11 BOLETALES
Boletaceae — Boletus, Leccinum, Phlebopus, Suillus, Tylopilus
Gomphidiaceae — Chroogomphus
Gyrodontaceae — Gyrodon, Gyroporus, Phaeogyroporus
Paxillaceae — Hygrophoropsis, Paxillus
Strobilomycetaceae — Afroboletus, Strobilomyces
Xerocomaceae — Boletellus, Phylloporus, Xerocomus

4-13-12 RUSSULALES
Russulaceae — Lactarius, Russula

4-14-1 SCLERODERMATALES
Sclerodermataceae — Scleroderma
Astraeaceae — Astraeus

4-14-3 TULOSTOMATALES
Tulostomataceae — Tulostoma

4-14-4 LYCOPERDALES
Broomeiaceae — Broomeia
Geastraceae — Geastrum
Lycoperdaceae — Calvatia, Langermannia, Lycoperdon

4-14-5 NIDULARIALES
Crucibulum

4-14-6 PHALLALES
Clathraceae — Clathrus, Lysurus
Phallaceae — Phallus

4-14-9 PODAXALES
Podaxaceae — Podaxis
Secotiaceae — Montagnea

4-16-1 USTILAGINALES
Ustilaginaceae — Tolyposporium, Ustilago

5-17 COELOMYCETES
Pestalotiopsis

5-18 HYPHOMYCETES
Aspergillus, Penicillium, Pseudoepicoccum

In this Systematic Listing of Eumycota (true fungi), species are arranged alphabetically within the Orders recognized by mycologists. Each has been given a numerical code, the elements of which identify the Subdivision, Class (or Subclass, in the case of *Ascomycotina*) and Order to which the fungus belongs. Species of *Amanita*, for example, have the code 4-13-10, where:

4 = *Basidiomycotina* (Subdivision)
13 = *Hymenomycetes* (Class)
10 = *Agaricales* (Order)

Some fungi are not, at present, classified below a certain rank. Species of this type have a "0" (zero) in the corresponding section(s) of their numerical code.

1 Subdivision   MASTIGOMYCOTINA
Fungi which produce spores and/or gametes capable of motion

1-10 Class   **Oomycetes**
1-10-4 Order   PERONOSPORALES

Sclerospora graminicola
   Niger 1044
   Senegal 749

3 Subdivision   ASCOMYCOTINA
Fungi whose spores develop within sac-like cells called asci

3-2 Subclass   **Laboulbeniomycetidae**
3-2-4 Order   CLAVICIPITALES

Cordyceps militaris = Scarlet Caterpillar Fungus
   Kuwait 958?
   Russia 4407

3-2-11 Order   ENDOMYCETALES

Saccharomyces sp = Yeast
   Japan 483

3-2-28 Order   PEZIZALES

Cookeina tricholoma
   Grenada 2035
   Togo 1896

Gyromitra esculenta = Beefsteak Morel, Elephant's Ears, False Morel, Lorchel, Turban Fungus
   Andorra 183
   Finland 859
   Germany (East Germany) E1654
   Hungary 3756

Morchella elata = High Morel
   Guinea-Bissau 925

Morchella esculenta (*Morchella conica*) = Common Morel, Edible Morel
   Andorra 177
   Canada 1334
   Denmark 665
   France 2788
   Great Britain 1383
   Guinea 917
   Hungary 3585
   Rumania 2589
   Vietnam 634

Morchella vulgaris = Common Morel
   Yugoslavia 2069

Phillipsia domingensis
   Christmas Island 189
   Fiji 674

Sarcoscypha coccinea (*Peziza coccinea*) = Moss Cups, Scarlet Elf Cup(s)
   Comoro Islands 583
   Tristan Da Cunha 372

Scutellinia virungae
   Zaire 946

Terfezia boudieri
   Djibouti Republic 1001

Terfezia leonis
   Algeria 847
   Kuwait 977

3-2-34 Order   SPHAERIALES

Engleromyces goetzei
   Zaire 945

Xylaria telfairei
   Zil Elwannyen Sesel 96

4 Subdivision   BASIDIOMYCOTINA
Fungi whose spores develop from club-shaped cells called basidia

4-13 Class   **Hymenomycetes**
4-13-1 Order   TREMELLALES = THE JELLY FUNGI

Phlogiotis helvelloides (*Tremiscus helvelloides*)
   Rumania 5070

Tremella fuciformis = Silver Ear, White Jelly Fungus
   China (People's Republic) 3092
   Congo (Brazzaville) 221

4-13-2 Order   AURICULARIALES

Auricularia polytricha = Ear Mushroom, Rat's Ear Fungus
   Philippines 2110
   Thailand 1267

4-13-6 Order   DACRYMYCETALES

Dacryopinax spathularia
   Fiji 670

4-13-8 Order   APHYLLOPHORALES

Clavulinopsis fusiformis (*Clavaria fusiformis*) = Golden
Spindles, Spindle Coral
  Canada 1331

Coltricia leonina (*Polystictus leoninus*)
  Burkina Faso 744
  Upper Volta 716

Coriolus sp
  Cameroun 750?

Coriolus hirsutus (*Trametes hirsuta*)
  Libya 1724

Coriolus versicolor (*Trametes versicolor*) = Many-zoned
Polypore
  Burkina Faso 748
  St. Helena 415
  Swaziland 464
  Upper Volta 720

Cymatoderma elegans var. *lamellata*
  Norfolk Island 303
  Vanuatu 377

Ganoderma applanatum = Artist's Fungus, Common
Ganoderma
  Lesotho 901
  Tuvalu 530

Ganoderma boninense
  Vanuatu 380

Ganoderma lucidum
  Burkina Faso 749
  Upper Volta 721

Ganoderma tornatum
  Samoa 697

Gomphus clavatus
  France 2787

Gomphus stereoides
  Rwanda 990

Haddowia longipes
  Christmas Island 188

Hericium erinaceus
  China (People's Republic) 3094

Hexagona tenuis
  Zil Elwannyen Sesel 98

Hydnum repandum = Hedgehog Fungus, Wood
Hedgehog, Wood Urchin
  St. Pierre et Miquelon 635

Laetiporus sulphureus (*Polyporus sulphureus*) = Chicken
Mushroom, Chicken of the Woods, Sulphur Polypore,
Sulphur Shelf
  Upper Volta **MS**722

Lentinus atrobrunneus
  Rwanda 989

Lentinus bertieri
  Grenada 1522

Lentinus crinitus
  Grenadines of Grenada MS1171

Lentinus cubensis
  Cuba 3404

Lentinus edodes (*Lentinula edodes*) = Black Mushroom,
Brown Mushroom, Shii-take Mushroom
  China (People's Republic) 3096
  Japan 1371
  Kenya 510
  Korea (North Korea) N862
  Philippines 2109

Lentinus retinervis
  Grenada 1523

Lentinus sajor-caju, (*Pleurotus sajor-caju*) = Abalone
Mushroom, Oyster Mushroom
  Kenya 506
  Philippines 2111
  Zil Elwannyen Sesel 97

Lentinus squarrosulus
  Djibouti Republic 1000
  Fiji 672

Lentinus tuber-regium
  Chad 773 774
  Lesotho 535

Lenzites elegans
  Zil Elwannyen Sesel 95

Lignosus rhinoceros
  Vanuatu 378

Microporus xanthopus
  Christmas Island 186

Mycobonia flava (*Hydnum brunneoleucum*)
  Samoa 699

Pleurotus sp
  Brazil 2108

Pleurotus cystidiosus = Abalone Mushroom
  Thailand 1268

Pleurotus eryngii
  Algeria 846

Pleurotus floridanus = Pink Oyster Mushroom
  Cuba 3402

Pleurotus levis
  Cuba 3401

Pleurotus ostreatus = Oyster Fungus, White Oyster
Mushroom
  Bulgaria 1280
  China (Taiwan) 1030
  Cuba 3405, 3406
  Thailand 1266
  Vietnam 628

Podoscypha elegans
  Rwanda 994

Podoscypha involuta
  Fiji 671

Polyporus induratus
St. Helena 417

Polyporus squamosus (*Melanopus squamosus, Polyporellus squamosus*) = Dryad's Saddle, Saddle-back Fungus, Sap Ball, Scaly Polypore
Vietnam 1159

Pycnoporus sanguineus (*Polyporus sanguineus*)
Brazil 2106
Nevis 486
Solomon Islands 515
Zaire 947

Ramaria aurea, (*Clavaria aurea*)
Rumania 2584

Ramaria botrytis, (*Clavariella botrytis*) = Cauliflower Clavaria
France 2302
Sweden 981

Ramaria moelleriana
Togo 1893
Zaire 951

Rigidoporus microporus
Tuvalu 533

Rigidoporus zonalis
Tuvalu 532

Schizophyllum commune = Split-gill, Wood Rot
Tuvalu 557
Uganda MS714

Sparassis crispa = Brain Fungus, Cauliflower Fungus, Sponge Fungus
Poland 2683

Stereum hirsutum = Hairy Stereum
Lesotho 903

Stereum ostrea = False Turkey Tail
Gambia 485
Vanuatu 379

Trametes cingulata
Tuvalu 556

Trametes ljubarskyi
Libya 1729

Trametes muelleri
Tuvalu 554

Tyromyces lignosus (*Leptoporus lignosus*)
Central African Republic 1038

4-13-9 Order   CANTHARELLALES

Cantharellus cibarius = Chanterelle, Pixie Stool, Yellow Chanterelle
Bulgaria 3413
Finland 860
Germany (East Germany) E2272
Guinea 919
Hungary 3587
Norway 1052
Poland 1091

Rumania 2592
Russia 3059
Rwanda 991
Sweden 979
Vietnam 631
Yugoslavia 2071

Cantharellus cinnabarinus = Cinnabar Chanterelle, Red Chanterelle, Vermilion Chanterelle
Antigua 1320
Barbuda 1165
Canada 1333
Dominica 1071
Nevis 488

Cantharellus infundibuliformis (*Cantharellus tubaeformis*) = Funnel-shaped Chanterelle
Norway 1004

Cantharellus miniatescens
Zaire 948
Zambia 423

Cantharellus rhodophyllus
Guinea 1162 1210

Craterellus cornucopioides (*Cantharellus cornucopioides*) = Black Trumpet, Death Trumpet, Horn of Plenty
France 2300

4-13-10 Order   AGARICALES = THE AGARICS

Agaricus arvensis (*Psalliota arvensis*) = Horse Mushroom
Niger 1062

Agaricus bisporus (*Psalliota bispora*) = Cultivated Mushroom, White Button Mushroom
China (People's Republic) 3097
China (Taiwan) 1029
Kenya 507 508
Korea (North Korea) N863

Agaricus campestris (*Psalliota campestris*) = Field Mushroom, Pink Bottoms
Burkina Faso 823
Germany (East Germany) E2269
Guinea 916
Hungary 3586
Maldive Islands 1220
Mongolia 329
Poland 1092
Rumania 2590
Uganda 713
Yugoslavia 2068

Agaricus niger (*Psalliota nigra*)
Guinea 1158 1206

Agaricus purpurellus (*Psalliota purpurella*)
Grenadines of Grenada MS1163

Agaricus rufoaurantiacus (*Psalliota rufoaurantiaca*)
Grenadines of Grenada 1166

Agaricus sebedulis (*Psalliota sebedulis*)
Central African Republic 137

Agaricus semotus (*Psalliota semota*)
Mali 1067

Agaricus silvaticus (*Psalliota silvatica*) = Red-staining Mushroom, Wood Mushroom
    Bulgaria 1275
    Vietnam 633

Agaricus xanthodermus (*Psalliota xanthoderma*) = Yellow Stainer
    Algeria 1028

Agrocybe cylindracea (*Pholiota aegerita*) = Agrocybe Mushroom
    Tristan Da Cunha 371

Agrocybe praecox var. *cutefracta* (*Pholiota praecox*) = Spring Agaric
    Tristan Da Cunha 369

Amanita caesarea = Caesar's Mushroom, Imperial Mushroom, Orange Agaric, Orange Amanita, Royal Agaric
    Albania 2450
    Bulgaria 1274
    Cuba 3403
    France 2299
    Kampuchea 612
    Libya 1723
    Rumania 2585
    San Marino 826
    Vietnam 635

Amanita citrina = False Death Cap
    Cuba 3312

Amanita curtipes
    Libya 1728

Amanita flammeola
    Zambia 420

Amanita lilloi
    Belize 962

Amanita muscaria = Fly Agaric
    Algeria 844
    Ciskei 143
    Cuba 3316
    Czechoslovakia 1061
    Germany (East Germany) E1653
    Hungary 3752
    Kampuchea 610
    Laos 814
    Maldive Islands 1219
    Mozambique 1120
    Poland 1093
    Russia 5652
    Sierra Leone MS1125

Amanita pantherina = False Blusher, Panther Cap, The Panther, Warted Agaric
    Botswana 535
    Ciskei 144
    Germany (East Germany) E1652
    Hungary 3755
    Kampuchea 608
    Maldive Islands 1221
    Russia 5653

Amanita phalloides = Deadly Amanite, Death Cap
    Algeria 845
    Benin 993
    Ciskei 141

    Czechoslovakia 2993
    Germany (East Germany) E1656
    Hungary 3751
    Mozambique 1122
    Poland 1087
    Russia 5651

Amanita robusta
    Guinea 1160 1208

Amanita rubescens = The Blusher
    Afghanistan 1030
    Bulgaria 3408
    Laos 817
    Libya 1736
    Rumania 5065

Amanita virosa = Destroying Angel
    Czechoslovakia 2994

Amanita zambiana
    Zambia 421

Armillaria luteobubalina
    Australia 825

Armillaria (*Armillariella*) *mellea* (*Armillaria polymyces*) = Boot-lace Fungus, Honey Fungus
    Bulgaria 1281
    Burkina Faso 826
    Comoro Islands 586
    Congo (Brazzaville) 1009
    Czechoslovakia 1062
    Hungary 3589
    Maldive Islands MS1225
    Rumania 2587

Bolbitius vitellinus = Yellow Cow-pat Toadstool
    Uganda MS714

Calocybe cyanocephala
    St. Lucia 1024

Chlorophyllum esculentum
    Central African Republic 1041?

Chlorophyllum molybdites = False Parasol, Green Gill
    Antigua 1318
    Ascension 333
    Barbuda 1163
    Chad 771 776
    Ciskei 142

Clitocybe dealbata (*Clitocybe rivulosa* subsp *dealbata*)
    Germany (East Germany) E1657

Clitocybe geotropa (*Clitocybe maxima*) = Trumpet Agaric
    Vietnam 1160

Clitocybe infundibuliformis (*Clitocybe gibba*) = Common Funnel Cap, Slender Funnel Fungus
    Guinea-Bissau 924

Clitocybe nebularis = Clouded Agaric, Clouded Clitocybe, New Cheese Agaric
    Great Britain 1039?
    Mali 1065
    Uganda 709

Clitopilus prunulus (*Paxillopsis prunulus*) = The Miller, Plum Clitopilus, Sweet-bread Mushroom
    San Marino 827

Collybia aurea
Grenadines of Grenada 1170

Collybia fusipes (*Collybia lancipes*) = Spindle Shank, Spool Foot
Guinea 912
Vietnam 1163

Collybia subpruinosa
Antigua 1044
Barbuda 911

Coprinus sp
Congo (Brazzaville) 1007

Coprinus angulatus
St. Helena 418

Coprinus atramentarius = Antabuse Ink Cap, Common Ink Cap, Grey Ink Cap
Afghanistan 1032
Congo (Brazzaville) 1007?
Vietnam 629

Coprinus comatus = Lawyer's Wig, Shaggy Caps, Shaggy Ink Cap
Australia 824
Botswana 533
Bulgaria 3411
Kampuchea 611
Laos 816
Maldive Islands 1222
Mongolia 327
Niger 1061
Rumania 2588

Coprinus domesticus
Norfolk Island 301

Coprinus micaceus = Glistening Ink Cap
Kampuchea 607

Cortinarius sp
Congo (Brazzaville) 1008

Cortinarius austrovenetus
Australia 826

Cortinarius cinnabarinus
Australia 823

Cortinarius herculeus
Libya 1734

Cortinarius mucosus
Congo (Brazzaville) 1008?

Cortinarius (*Leprocybe*) *orellanus*
Czechoslovakia 2995

Cortinarius (*Phlegmacium*) *subfulgens*
Libya 1725

Cortinarius (*Sericeocybe*) *traganus* = Goaty Smell Cortinarius
Monaco 1892

Cortinarius violaceus
Vietnam 1164

Crinipellis sp
New Zealand 1463?

Crinipellis perniciosus (*Marasmius perniciosus*) = Witches' Broom of Cacao
Trinidad and Tobago 773

Cyptotrama asprata (*Xerulina asprata*)
Malawi 723

Cystolepiota eriophora (*Lepiota eriophora*)
Grenada MS1525

Dermocybe pratensis
Libya 1726

Eccilia cystiophorus
Dominica 1073
Grenada 1524

Entoloma cystidiophorum
Grenada 1524?

Entoloma sinuata (*Rhodophyllus sinuatus*) = Leaden Entoloma, Livid Entoloma
Germany (East Germany) E1650

Filoboletus manipularis
Solomon Islands 516

Flammulina velutipes (*Collybia velutipes*) = Golden Mushroom, The Velvet Foot, Velvet Shank, Winter Fungus
China (Taiwan) 1032
Vietnam 630

Galerina marginata
Czechoslovakia 2996

Galerina mutabilis (*Kuehneromyces mutabilis*, *Pholiota mutabilis*) = Changeable Agaric, Changing Pholiota
Burkina Faso 820
Maldive Islands 1218

Gerronema citrinum
St. Lucia 1022

Gerronema schusteri
Falkland Islands 550

Gymnopilus chrysopellus
Dominica MS1075
Nevis 487

Gymnopilus junonius (*Gymnopilus spectabilis* va junonia, *Pholiota spectabilis*)
Kampuchea 606
Maldive Islands 1223

Hebeloma crustuliniforme = Fairy Cake Hebeloma, Fairy Cake Mushroom, Poison Pie
Kampuchea 609

Hygrocybe acutoconica
St. Kitts 244

Hygrocybe firma
Grenadines of Grenada 766 1165
Togo 1894

Hygrocybe hypohaemacta
Grenada 2033

Hygrocybe martinicensis
Grenadines of Grenada **MS**1171

Hygrocybe nigrescens (*Hygrocybe pseudoconica,*
Hygrophorus nigrescens) = Blackening Wax Cap
Grenada 2037

Hygrocybe occidentalis (*Hygrophorus occidentalis*)
Grenada 2031
Grenadines of St. Vincent 479
St. Kitts 241

Hygrocybe occidentalis var. *scarletina*
Antigua 1042
Barbuda 909

Hygrocybe punicea (*Hygrophorus puniceus*) = Crimson
Wax Cap, Red Hygrophorus, Scarlet Wax Gill
Monaco 1889

Hygrophorus adonis (*Camarophyllus adonis*)
Falkland Islands 549

Hygrophorus pratensis (*Camarophyllus pratensis*) = Buff
Cap, Meadow Hygrophorus
St. Pierre et Miquelon 587

Hypholoma sp
Afghanistan 1033
United States of America 2267?

Hypholoma fasciculare (*Geophila fascicularis,*
Naematoloma fasciculare) = Clustered Woodlover,
Sulphur Tuft
Burkina Faso 821
Comoro Islands 584
Cuba 3317
Maldive Islands 1217
Niger 1060
Russia 5655

Inocybe patouillardii = Red-staining Inocybe
Cuba 3315
Germany (East Germany) E1655
Hungary 3753

Laccaria tetraspora
Tristan Da Cunha 370

Lepiota clypeolaria = Shield Fungus
Rumania 5068

Lepiota cortinarius
Mali 1066

Lepiota esculenta
Central African Republic 1041

Lepiota procera (*Leucocoprinus procerus, Macrolepiota*
procera) = Parasol Mushroom
Albania 2451
Algeria 1029
Bulgaria 1279
Czechoslovakia 1058
Finland 938
Guinea 918
Hungary 3588
Laos 819
Mali 1068
Rumania 2583

San Marino 828
Sweden 978

Lepiota pseudoignicolor
Grenada 2034

Lepiota rhacodes (*Macrolepiota rhacodes*) = Shaggy
Parasol
Uganda 710

Lepiota roseolamellata
Grenada 1521

Lepiota spiculata
St. Lucia 1023

Lepiota subradicans
Guinea 1161 1209

Lepista caffrorum
Lesotho 532

Lepista nuda (*Rhodopaxillus nudus, Tricholoma nudum*)
= Blue Leg, Bluette, Naked Mushroom, Wood Blewit(s)
Guinea-Bissau 926
Mozambique 1123
Norway 1040
Uganda 711

Leptonia caeruleocapitata = Blue Cap
Antigua 1316
Barbuda 1161
Grenadines of Grenada **MS**770

Leptonia howellii
Grenadines of Grenada 1167

Leucoagaricus excoriatus (*Macrolepiota excoriata*)
Libya 1727

Leucocoprinus africanus
Central African Republic 133

Leucocoprinus birnbaumii
Trinidad and Tobago 772

Leucocoprinus brebissonii (*Lepiota brebissonii*)
Antigua 1045
Barbuda 912

Leucocoprinus cepaestripes
Ascension 334
Upper Volta **MS**722

Leucocoprinus fragilissimus (*Lepiota licmophora*)
Christmas Island 185
Grenadines of St. Vincent 478

Leucopaxillus gracillimus = Slender Stalk
Antigua **MS**1321
Barbuda **MS**1166
Grenada 2036
Malawi 720

Leucopaxillus lepistoides
Libya 1722

Limacella guttata
Malawi 721

Macrolepiota imbricata
Djibouti Republic 999

Macrolepiota zeyheri = White Parasol Mushroom
Ciskei 108

Marasmiellus distantifolius
Ascension 336

Marasmiellus inoderma
Solomon Islands 514

Marasmiellus purpureus
Grenadines of Grenada 1168

Marasmius sp
New Zealand 1463?

Marasmius arborescens (*Synpodia arborescens*)
Central African Republic 134

Marasmius echinosphaerus
Ascension 332

Marasmius haematocephalus = Red Pinwheel
Antigua 1319
Barbuda 1164
Grenada 2032
St. Kitts 242

Marasmius niveus
Norfolk Island 302

Marasmius oreades = Clover Windling, Fairy Ring
Champignon, Scotch Bonnet
Andorra 186
Hungary 3584

Marasmius pallescens
Grenadines of St.Vincent 477

Marasmius scorodonius = Garlic Marasmius
Burkina Faso 825

Marasmius trinitatis
Grenadines of Grenada 1169

Mycena sp
Falkland Islands 548
Rwanda 995

Mycena chlorophos
Samoa 698

Mycena holoporphyra
Grenada MS2039

Mycena pura = Lilac Fairy Helmet, Lilac Mycena
Antigua 1313
Barbuda 1158

Nolanea verna
Czechoslovakia 2992

Omphalotus olearius (*Clitocybe illudens, Pleurotus olearius*) = False Chanterelle, Jack O'Lantern,
Olive-wood Pleurotus
France 2301
Hungary 3754
Uganda 707

Oudemansiella radicata (*Collybia radicata, Mucidula radicata*) = Rooting Shank
Uganda 708

Panaeolus antillarum
Nevis 485

Panaeolus papilionaceus
Norfolk Island 300

Pholiota aurivella
Libya 1730

Pholiota flammans
Monaco 1890

Pholiota lenta
Libya 1735

Pholiota spumosa (*Flammula spumosa*)
Mongolia 1120

Pluteus brunneisucus
St. Helena 416

Pluteus cervinus = Common Fawn Agaric, Deer
Mushroom
Maldive Islands 1224

Psathyrella tuberculata = Rough Psathyrella
Antigua 1314
Barbuda 1159

Psilocybe caerulescens
Belize 966

Psilocybe cubensis = Golden Tops
Antigua 1315
Barbuda 1160
St. Kitts 243

Pyrrhoglossum pyrrhum
Antigua MS1046
Barbuda MS913

Rhodophyllus callidermus
Guinea 1157 1205

Rozites caperata (*Cortinarius caporatus, Pholiota caperata*) = The Gypsy, Wrinkled Pholiota
Finland 939
Norway 1005

Stropharia aeruginosa = Verdigris Agaric
Maldive Islands MS1225

Termitomyces spp = Beefsteak Mushroom, Termite
Mushroom
Ciskei 109

Termitomyces aurantiacus
Central African Republic 1042
Congo (Brazzaville) 219

Termitomyces entolomoides
Congo (Brazzaville) 217

Termitomyces eurrhizus
Malawi 722

Termitomyces globulus
  Guinea 1159 1207

Termitomyces letestui
  Central African Republic 1040
  Zambia 422

Termitomyces mammiformis
  Congo (Brazzaville) 220

Termitomyces microcarpus
  Congo (Brazzaville) 218

Termitomyces robustus
  Central African Republic 1043

Termitomyces schimperi = Termite Mushroom
  Central African Republic 136
  Kenya 509

Tricholoma gambosum (*Calocybe gambosa, Lyophyllum* (*Calocybe*) *georgii*) = St. George's Mushroom
  San Marino 831

Tricholoma lobayensis
  Central African Republic MS1044

Tricholoma matsutake (*Armillaria matsutake*) = Matsu-take Mushroom, Pine Mushroom
  Korea (North Korea) N861

Tricholoma terreum
  Vietnam 1161

Tricholoma terreum
  Vietnam 1161

Tricholoma virgatum
  St. Pierre et Miquelon 609

Tricholomopsis rutilans (*Tricholoma rutilans*) = Plums and Custard, Purple Blewit
  Afghanistan 1028

Trogia anthidepas
  Christmas Island 187

Trogia buccinalis
  Antigua 1043
  Barbuda 910

Volvariella cubensis
  Grenadines of Grenada 768

Volvariella esculenta (*Volvaria esculenta*)
  Congo (Brazzaville) 216

Volvariella volvacea = Chinese Mushroom, Padi Straw Mushroom, Straw Mushroom
  Antigua MS1321
  Barbuda MS1166
  Philippines 2112
  Thailand 1265
  Vietnam 632

Xeromphalina tenuipes = Brown Cap
  Antigua 1317
  Barbuda 1162
  Grenada MS2039
  Rwanda 993
  Trinidad and Tobago 770

4-13-11 Order   BOLETALES = THE BOLETES

Afroboletus luteolus
  Lesotho 534

Boletellus cubensis
  Belize 964
  Dominica 1072
  St. Kitts 245

Boletellus mirabilis (*Boletus mirabilis*) = Admirable Boletus
  Canada 1332

Boletus sp
  Niger 1059

Boletus aereus (*Tubiporus aereus*) = Bronze Boletus
  Vietnam 1165

Boletus calopus (*Boletus pachypus*) = Scarlet-stemmed Boletus
  Nicaragua 2649?

Boletus edulis = Cep, Edible Mushroom, Penny Bun, Stone Mushroom
  Albania 2452
  Andorra 195
  Benin 992
  Botswana 536
  Bulgaria 1277
  Ciskei 107
  Comoro Islands 582
  Czechoslovakia 1059
  Finland 861
  Germany (East Germany) E2271
  Guinea 914
  Hungary 3583
  Laos 815
  Libya 1731
  Niger 1059?
  Poland 1089
  Rumania 2591
  Russia 3060
  San Marino 829
  Sierra Leone 1124
  Swaziland 465
  Sweden 980
  Yugoslavia 2070

Boletus erythropus (*Boletus miniatoporus*) = Flaky-stemmed Witches' Mushroom, Red-stalked Boletus
  Afghanistan 1029
  Germany (East Germany) E2268

Boletus luridus = Oak Mushroom
  Nicaragua 2650?
  Rumania 5066

Boletus regius = Royal Boletus
  Bulgaria 3409

Boletus satanas = Devil's Boletus, Satan's Boletus, Satan's Mushroom
  Algeria 1027
  Cuba 3311
  Denmark 666
  Germany (East Germany) E1651

Chroogomphus rutilus (Gomphidius rutilus, Gomphidius viscidus)
Andorra 217
Guinea-Bissau 929

Gyrodon merulioides
Nicaragua 2652?

Gyroporus castaneus (Boletus castaneus) = Chestnut Boletus
Nicaragua 2654?

Gyroporus cyanescens (Boletus cyanescens) = Indigo Boletus
France 2786

Hygrophoropsis aurantiaca (Cantharellus aurantiacus) = False Chanterelle
Palau 252?

Leccinum aurantiacum (Boletus aurantiacus)
Afghanistan 1034
Bulgaria 3410
Mongolia 1116
Russia 3061

Leccinum rotundifoliae
Monaco 1888

Leccinum scabrum (Boletus scaber, Trachypus scaber) = Brown Birch Bolete, Cow Fungus, Rough-stemmed Boletus, Shaggy Boletus
Afghanistan 1031
Burkina Faso 824
Mongolia 1117
Poland 1094

Leccinum versipelle (Boletus testaceoscaber, Boletus versipellis, Krombholzia rufescens, Leccinum testaceoscabrum) = Orange Birch Bolete, Orange Cap Boletus, Red Cap
Czechoslovakia 1060
Finland 968
Germany (East Germany) E2267
Mongolia 1116?

Paxillus involutus = Brown Roll-rim, Inrolled Paxil
Benin 994
Cuba 3314
Laos 820
Lesotho 900

Phaeogyroporus silvaticus (Phlebopus silvaticus)
Guinea MS1163 MS1211

Phaeogyroporus sudanicus (Phlebopus sudanicus)
Central African Republic 135 1039

Phlebopus colossus sudanicus
Burkina Faso 746
Upper Volta 718

Phylloporus ampliporus
Zaire 944

Strobilomyces floccopus (Boletus floccopus, Boletus strobilaceus, Strobilomyces strobilaceus) = Cone-like Boletus, Old Man of the Woods
Poland 2681

Strobilomyces retisporus
Nicaragua 2648?

Suillus bovinus (Boletus bovinus) = Cow Boletus, Jersey Cow Bolete
Swaziland 462

Suillus granulatus (Boletus granulatus, Ixocomus granulatus) = Granulated Boletus
Burkina Faso 822
Lesotho 902
Mongolia 331
Uganda 706

Suillus grevillei (Boletus elegans) = Elegant Boletus, Larch Bolete
Bulgaria 1276

Suillus luteus (Boletus luteus) = Butter Mushroom, Slippery Jack, Yellow-brown Boletus
Afghanistan 1063
Falkland Islands 547
Norway 1053
Poland 1088
Russia 3058
Uganda 712

Suillus variegatus (Boletus variegatus, Ixocomus variegatus) = Variegated Boletus
Mongolia 334 1114

Tylopilus felleus (Boletus felleus) = Bitter Bolete
Cuba 3313
Russia 5654

Tylopilus plumbeoviolaceus
Nicaragua 2653?

Xerocomus badius (Boletus badius, Suillus badius) = Bay Boletus, Chestnut Boletus , Chestnut Mushroom
Germany (East Germany) E2270

Xerocomus coccolobae
Grenadines of Grenada 767

Xerocomus guadelupae
Dominica 1074

Xerocomus hypoxanthus
Grenadines of St. Vincent 480

Xerocomus illudens
Nicaragua 2651?

Xerocomus parasiticus (Boletus parasiticus)
Poland 2680

Xerocomus subtomentosus (Boletus subtomentosus) = Downy Boletus
Laos 818

4-13-12 Order   RUSSULALES

Lactarius deliciosus = Saffron Milk Cap
Algeria 1030
Botswana 534
Bulgaria 1278
Guinea 915
Guinea-Bissau 927

Mongolia 333
Mozambique 1121
Poland 1090
Rumania 2586
Russia 3062
Sierra Leone 1123

Lactarius deterrimus
Finland 937
Norway 1041

Lactarius lignyotus
Monaco 1891

Lactarius phlebonemus
Zaire 949

Lactarius piperatus (Lactarius pergamenus) = Peppery
Milk Cap
Rumania 5067

Lactarius putidus
Grenadines of Grenada 769

Lactarius resimus
Mongolia 1119

Lactarius sanguifluus
Andorra 166

Lactarius scobiculatus
Mongolia 332

Lactarius torminosus = Griping Toadstool, Shaggy Milk
Cap, Woolly Milk Cap
Finland 967
Mongolia 328

Russula aurata = Golden Russula
Vietnam 1162

Russula capensis = Cape Russula
Ciskei 110

Russula claroflava (Russula flava) = Yellow Swamp
Russula
Mongolia 1118

Russula cyanoxantha = Blue Russula, The Charcoal
Burner, Green Agaric
Mongolia 1115
Rumania 5069
Sierra Leone 1121

Russula decolorans
Sweden 976

Russula delica (Russula brevipes) = Milk-white Russula
Mongolia 330

Russula olivacea
Monaco 1893

Russula paludosa
Finland 969
St. Pierre et Miquelon 598
San Marino 830

Russula puiggarii
Belize 969
St. Lucia 1025

Russula rubra
China (People's Republic) 3095

Russula sanguinea
Libya 1733

Russula vesca = Bare-toothed Russula
Bulgaria 3412

Russula virescens = Cracked Green Russula
France 2789
Guinea-Bissau 928

4-14 Class   **Gasteromycetes**
4-14-1 Order   SCLERODERMATALES = THE
                    EARTH-BALLS

Astraeus hygrometricus (Geastrum hygrometricum)
Comoro Islands 585

*Scleroderma citrinum (Scleroderma aurantium,
Scleroderma vulgare)* = Common Earth-ball
Poland 2680

Scleroderma flavidum
Fiji 673
Lesotho MS904

Scleroderma polyrhizum
Libya 1737

4-14-3 Order   TULOSTOMA IALES

Tulostoma volvulatum
Chad 772

4-14-4 Order   LYCOPERDALES = THE PUFF-BALLS

Broomeia congregata
Lesotho 533

Calvatia sp
Brazil 2107

Calvatia gardneri
Solomon Islands 513

Geastrum sp
Rwanda 988

*Geastrum sessile (Geastrum fimbriatum, Geastrum
rufescens)*
Libya 1732
Niger 1063

*Langermannia gigantea (Calvatia gigantea, Lasiosphaera
gigantea, Lycoperdon giganteum)* = Giant Puff-ball
Poland 2684
Swaziland 463

Lycoperdon marginatum
Ascension 335

Lycoperdon perlatum (Lycoperdon gemmatum) =
Common Puff-ball, Devil's Tobacco Pouch, Poor Man's
Sweetbread
Guinea 913
Sierra Leone 1122
Sweden 977

4-14-5 Order   NIDULARIALES = BIRD'S NEST FUNGI

Crucibulum laeve (*Crucibulum vulgare*) = Common Bird's
Nest
   Congo (Brazzaville) 1011

4-14-6 Order   PHALLALES

Clathrus cancellatus
   Albania 2453

Clathrus crispus
   Grenada 2038

Clathrus ruber
   Poland 2679

Lysurus corallocephalus (*Kalchbrennera corallocephala*)
   Togo 1895

Phallus sp (*Dictyophora* sp)
   Congo (Brazzaville) 1010

Phallus hadriani (*Dictyophora hadriani*)
   Poland 2682

Phallus indusiatus (*Dictyophora indusiata*) = Veiled
Stinkhorn
   China (People's Republic) 3093
   China (Taiwan) 1031
   Congo (Brazzaville) 1010?
   Palau 255
   Samoa 696
   Trinidad and Tobago 771
   Upper Volta MS722
   Zaire 950

4-14-9 Order   PODAXALES

Montagnea (*Montagnites*) *candollei*
   Kuwait 976

Podaxis pistillaris
   Chad 775
   Grenadines of Grenada 1164

4-16 Class   **Ustilaginomycetes**
4-16-1 Order   USTILAGINALES = THE SMUTS

Tolyposporium ehrenbergii
   Niger 1044

Tolyposporium penicillariae = Pearl Millet Smut
   Senegal 749

Ustilago maydis = Maize Smut
   Mexico 1914

5 Subdivision   DEUTEROMYCOTINA

Fungi Imperfecti – fungi which cannot reproduce sexually,
but in which a parasexual cycle may occur

5-17 Class   **Coelomycetes**

Pestalotiopsis palmarum = Grey Leaf Spot
   Tuvalu 555

5-18 Class   **Hyphomycetes**

Aspergillus dybowskii var. *laevispora* (*Stilbothamnium
dybowskii* var. *laevispora*)
   Rwanda 992

Penicillium glaucum
   Monaco 1117

Penicillium notatum = Penicillin*
   Austria 1972
   Congo (Brazzaville) 494 613
   Djibouti Republic 795
   Gabon 677
   Great Britain 753
   Mauritius 552 553 554 555
   Niger 864
   Wallis and Futuna Islands 363
* Penicillin is a group of antibiotic substances produced
by *Penicillium notatum* and *P chrysogenum*. Many other
stamps commemorate Sir Alexander Fleming and the
discovery or administering of Penicillin, but do not show the
substance itself.

Pseudoepicoccum cocos = Brown Leaf Spot
   Tuvalu 531

Lichens

Lichens are dual organisms comprising a fungus (the "mycobiont") and an alga or cyanobacterium (the "photobiont") in association. About 18,000 species have been identified. The fungus is usually an *Ascomycete*, though a few *Hymenomycetes* and *Deuteromycetes* are also lichenized. The algae commonly belong to the blue-green *Cyanobacteria* or *Cyanophyta* (such as *Nostoc*), or the green algae or *Chlorophyta* (such as *Trebouxia*). The shape and form of the lichen body (the "thallus") is generally determined by the fungus; the algae are either suspended throughout the thallus or embedded in a compact layer below the outer cortex. The relationship is comparable with *Mycorrhizas*: the algae obtain protection, water and minerals from their host, which they provide with growth substances and the products of photosynthesis. Blue-green photobionts can fix atmospheric nitrogen which is also passed on to the fungus. Asexual reproduction may be by fragmentation, budding or the release of powdery structures ("soredia") comprising a few algal cells surrounded by threads of fungus. The mycobiont may reproduce sexually by releasing spores, but these must encounter an alga or cyanobacterium if a new lichen is to form.

Lichens are probably the slowest growing of all life-forms, mature specimens increasing at a rate of only 1 millimetre or less each year. They can survive in extremely harsh conditions and are amongst the first plants to colonize bare rock, eventually providing the soil in which higher plants can root. Their exceptional durability has given rise to lichenometry, a technique for studying the age of rock surfaces. They are used for food, both by animals (such as Reindeer moss) and Man (such as Rock Tripe). Other applications include dyeing (such as cudbear, crottle, orchil), medicine and perfumery. Lichens are also important indicators of pollution.

Stamps depicting lichens are listed below (i) in order of issuing country and (ii) in a systematic listing which, because they are classified according to their fungal component, supplements the systematic listing for fungi.

Countries Section

BRITISH ANTARCTIC TERRITORY
Antarctica
100 pence = 1 pound

1989

167 10p *Xanthoria elegans*
168 24p *Usnea aurantiaco-atra*
169 29p *Cladonia chlorophaea*
170 58p *Umbilicaria antarctica*

Set of 4   2·10   2·40

FIJI
South Pacific
100 cents = 1 dollar

1983

654† 70c Red Shining Parrot with *Hypogymnia physodes*? and *Usnea* sp? . . . .   1·25   1·00

COLLECT BIRDS ON STAMPS
Second revised edition of this Stanley Gibbons thematic catalogue. Now available at £8.50 (p.+ p. £2.75) from: Stanley Gibbons Publications Ltd, 5 Parkside, Christchurch Road, Ringwood, Hants BH24 3SH.

FRENCH SOUTHERN AND ANTARCTIC TERRITORIES
Antarctica and nearby islands
100 centimes = 1 franc

1987

222† 6f50 *Neuropogon taylori* (*Usnea taylori*) . . . .   1·40   1·40

GREAT BRITAIN
North-West Europe
100 pence = 1 pound

1977

1041† 9p Eurasian Red Squirrel with *Evernia prunastri*   25   20

ISLE OF MAN
North-west Europe
100 pence = 1 pound

1986

317† 12p *Usnea articulata*   35   35

JAMAICA
West Indies
100 cents = 1 dollar

1979

472† 50c Jamaican Woodpecker with *Parmelia*? or *Hypogymnia* sp? .   70   15

1982

565† $1 *Usnea* sp? and *Parmelia*? or *Hypogymnia* sp?   80   80
566† $1 *Usnea* sp? and *Parmelia*? or *Hypogymnia* sp?   80   80
567† $1 *Usnea* sp?   80   80

LIECHTENSTEIN
Central Europe
100 rappen = 1 franc

1981

771† 40r *Xanthoria parietina*   25   25

| 772† | 50r *Parmelia physodes* (*Hypogymnia physodes*) . . . . | 30 | 30 |

| 2289† | 22c Pikas with *Xanthoria* sp? . . | 35 | 10 |
| 2293† | 22c Mountain Goat with a number of crustose lichens, including *Xanthoria* sp . . . . | 35 | 10 |

NEW ZEALAND
Australasia
100 cents = 1 dollar

1982

| 1290† | 45c New Zealand Falcon with *Parmelia* sp . . . . | 60 | 20 |
| 1292† | $1 Kokako with *Parmelia* sp . . . | 65 | 20 |

SWEDEN
Northern Europe
100 ore = 1 krona

1984

| 1216† | 1k60 Greater Spotted Woodpecker with *Parmelia* sp . . . . | 45 | 40 |
| 1217† | 1k60 European Nuthatch with *Parmelia* sp possibly *Parmelia caperata* . . . . | 45 | 40 |

UNITED STATES OF AMERICA
North America
100 cents = 1 dollar

1987

URUGUAY
South America
1000 milesimos = 100 centesimos = 1 peso

1988

| 1945† | 30p *Usnea densirostra* . . . . . | 20 | 15 |

Systematic Listing

3-2-21   *Cladonia chlorophaea*
British Antarctic Territory 169

Evernia prunastri
Great Britain 1041

Hypogymnia sp
Jamaica 472? 565? 566?

Hypogymnia physodes
syn. *Parmelia physodes*
Fiji 654?
Liechtenstein 772

Parmelia sp
Jamaica 472? 565? 566?
New Zealand 1290 1292
Sweden 1216

Parmelia caperata
Sweden 1217?

Umbilicaria antarctica
British Antarctic Territory 170

Usnea sp
Fiji 654?
Jamaica 565? 566? 567?

Usnea articulata
Isle of Man 317

Usnea aurantiaco-atra
British Antarctic Territory 168

Usnea densirostra
Uruguay 1945

Usnea taylori
syn. *Neuropogon taylori*
French Southern and Antarctic Territories 22

3-2-36   *Xanthoria* sp
United States of America 2289? 2293

Xanthoria elegans
British Antarctic Territory 167

Xanthoria parietina
Liechtenstein 771

Mycorrhizas

A Mycorrhiza (literally "Fungus-root") is a dual organism resulting from the association of a fungus with the roots of a plant. The relationship is mutually beneficial : the plant absorbs mineral salts, notably phosphate, through the fungus, which in turn obtains the carbon it needs for growth and respiration from the photosynthate of the plant.

In temperate and boreal regions, the predominent form of such mutualism is the ectomycorrhiza of forest trees with different Basidiomycetes. Over 5,000 species of fungi are involved, especially *Agaricales*, *Boletales* and *Russulales* (4-13-10 to 12). Some associate with only one species of tree, others with several species from one or more families.

In ectomycorrhizas the fungus associates by enveloping, rather than penetrating, the roots of its host (cf. endomycorrhizas, ectendomyco-rhizas). They enable trees to establish in poorer soils and can be crucial to the success of afforestation. In southern Chile, for example, new plantations of non-indigenous pines fail unless the ground is impregnated with the mycelium of the Yellow-brown Boletus (*Suillus luteus*).

A list of mycorrhizal associations is given below. Each family and species of tree is identified by its systematic and common names, and the fungi with which it associates are listed underneath. Only those fungi which appear on stamps have been included (for a more extensive listing, see Trappe, *Botanical Review* vol. 28 pp. 538-606 (1962)). Catalogue numbers refer to stamps which illustrate either a listed species of tree, or other species which are also mycorrhizal. The intention has been to provide a general guide to mycorrhizal trees, rather than a comprehensive listing. Most stamps depicting paintings of trees, for example, have been excluded, as well as many of those which concentrate on leaves, flowers or fruit.

MYCORRHIZAL ASSOCIATIONS, BY TREE

ABIES spp (The Silver Firs)
> FUNGI: *Suillus luteus*; *Tricholoma matsutake*

Algeria 836
Greece 1151
Mongolia 1462
Spain 2143

A. alba (Common or European Silver Fir)
> FUNGI: *Amanita citrina*, *muscaria*, *pantherina*; *Cantharellus cibarius*, *infundibuliformis*; *Xerocomus badius*

Italy 1883
Liechtenstein 755 906
Norway 798

ACER spp (The Maples)
> FUNGI: *Boletus erythropus*; *Hebeloma crustuliniforme*; *Leccinum aurantiacum*

Canada 877
Poland 2556
San Marino 1128
United States of America 2286 2305
Yugoslavia 1860

A. campestre (Field or Hedge Maple)
> FUNGUS: *Leccinum scabrum*

Liechtenstein 369

ALNUS spp (The Alders)
> FUNGUS: *Russula decolorans*

Yugoslavia 929 1862 1862a

BETULA spp (The Birches)
> FUNGI: *Lactarius resimus*; *Russula sanguinea*, *vesca*, *virescens*

Iceland 351
Mongolia 1466
United States of America 1739

B. pendula = B. alba = B. verrucosa (European White or Silver Birch)
> FUNGI: *Amanita muscaria*; *Boletus edulis*, *subtomentosus*; *Lactarius torminosus*; *Leccinum aurantiacum*, *scabrum*, *versipelle*; *Russula claroflava*

Andorra F330
Belgium 2147
Finland 723
Liechtenstein 357
Norway 799
Poland 2561
United States of America 2267

B. pubescens = *B. tortuosa* (Downy Birch)

FUNGI: *Amanita muscaria*; *Lactarius torminosus*; *Leccinum aurantiacum, scabrum*; *Paxillus involutus*

Ireland 585

CASTANEA spp (The Chestnuts)

C. sativa = *C. vesca* (Spanish or Sweet Chestnut)

FUNGI: *Amanita caesarea, rubescens*; *Boletus edulis, luridus, regius*; *Cantharellus cibarius*; *Gyroporus castaneus*; *Leccinum aurantiacum, scabrum*; *Russula cyanoxantha, rubra, vesca*; *Tylopilus felleus*; *Xerocomus badius, subtomentosus*

Andorra F360
Monaco 1804 1805 1806 1807
Rumania 3079
Spain 2302

CEDRUS spp (The Cedars)

C. atlantica (Atlas Cedar)

FUNGUS: *Cortinarius herculeus*

Algeria 788
French Morocco 219 220 233
Great Britain 1505

C. libanii (Cedar of Lebanon)

FUNGUS: *Amanita pantherina*

Cyprus 525
Lebanon 58, etc.
Russia 2739
San Marino 1121
Saudi Arabia 377 378
Turkey 2880

CORYLUS spp (The Hazels)

FUNGI: *Boletus erythropus, Leccinum aurantiacum*

C. avellana (European Hazel or Cobnut)

FUNGI: *Amanita rubescens*; *Boletus edulis*; *Cortinarius violaceus*; *Gyroporus cyanescens*; *Hydnum repandum*; *Lactarius piperatus*; *Leccinum scabrum*; *Lepista nuda*; *Strobilomyces floccopus*; *Xerocomus subtomentosus*

Aland Islands 17
Germany (West Berlin) B583
Monaco 1766 1767 1768 1769

EUCALYPTUS spp (The Eucalypts or Gums)

FUNGUS: *Lycoperdon perlatum*

Ascension 374
Australia 422 665 870 871 872 873 874
Brazil 1829a
St. Helena 226 231 236 265 270
San Marino 1126

FAGUS spp (The Beeches)

F. sylvatica (Common Beech)

FUNGI: *Amanita caesarea, citrina, muscaria, pantherina, phalloides, rubescens*; *Boletus calopus, edulis, erythropus, luridus, regius, satanas*; *Cantharellus cibarius, infundibuliformis*; *Clitopilus prunulus*; *Craterellus cornucopioides*; *Entoloma sinuata*; *Gyroporus cyanescens*; *Hydnum repandum*; *Lactarius piperatus, resimus, scobiculatus*; *Leccinum*

scabrum; *Paxillus involutus*; *Ramaria aurea*; *Russula aurata, cyanoxantha, delica, olivacea, rubra, vesca, virescens*; *Strobilomyces floccopus*; *Tricholoma terreum*; *Xerocomus subtomentosus*

Belgium 2146
France 2689
Germany (West Germany) 1905
Liechtenstein 401 754 756

FRAXINUS spp (The Ashes)

FUNGI: *Boletus edulis*; *Clitopilus prunulus*

Aland Islands 17
Russia 5048

LARIX spp (The Larches)

FUNGUS: *Lactarius deliciosus*

L. decidua = *L. europaea* = *L. polonica* = *L. sudetica* (Common or European Larch)

FUNGI: *Amanita muscaria*; *Boletus edulis, erythropus*; *Lepiota procera*; *Paxillus involutus*; *Suillus grevillei, luteus, variegatus*

Germany (West Berlin) B582
Liechtenstein 375
Yugoslavia 1858

L. sibirica (Siberian Larch)

FUNGUS: *Suillus grevillei*

Mongolia 1464
San Marino 1125

PICEA spp (The Spruces)

FUNGUS: *Tricholoma matsutake*

Mongolia 1467
St. Pierre et Miquelon 415
Turkey 2878

P. abies = *Abies excelsa* = *P. excelsa* (Norway Spruce)

FUNGI: *Amanita citrina, muscaria, pantherina, phalloides*; *Boletus edulis*; *Cantharellus cibarius, infundibuliformis*; *Clitocybe dealbata*; *Clitopilus prunulus*; *Craterellus cornucopioides*; *Geastrum sessile*; *Hydnum repandum*; *Lactarius deliciosus, scobiculatus*; *Leccinum aurantiacum*; *Lepiota rhacodes*; *Lycoperdon perlatum*; *Paxillus involutus*; *Ramaria aurea*; *Russula delica, olivacea, paludosa, rubra*; *Suillus bovinus, granulatus, luteus*; *Tricholoma terreum*; *Tylopilus felleus*; *Xerocomus badius, subtomentosus*

Finland 725
France 2692
Iceland 350
Liechtenstein 355 907
Norway 797
Rumania 3078

PINUS spp (The Pines)

P. banksiana (Jack Pine)

FUNGI: *Amanita pantherina*; *rubescens*; *Suillus luteus*

Canada 585

P. caribaea (Caribbean Pine)

FUNGI: *Leccinum scabrum*; *Suillus bovinus, granulatus, grevillei, luteus, variegatus*

Cuba 2226
Dominican Republic 665

P. cembra = *P. sibirica* (Arolla Pine)

FUNGI: *Amanita muscaria; Lactarius deliciosus; Paxillus involutus*

Mongolia 1461

P. densiflora (Japanese Red Pine)

FUNGI: *Lentinus edodes; Suillus bovinus, granulatus, luteus; Tricholoma matsutake*

Japan 1254 1350

P. mugo = *P. montana* (Mountain Pine)

FUNGI: *Amanita citrina, muscaria, pantherina, rubescens; Boletus edulis; Lactarius deliciosus; Suillus granulatus, luteus, variegatus; Tricholoma virgatum; Xerocomus subtomentosus*

Germany (West Germany) 1908
Liechtenstein 403

P. pinaster (Bournemouth or Maritime Pine)

FUNGI: *Lactarius deliciosus; Suillus bovinus, granulatus*

Spain 2145

P. pinea (Italian Stone or Umbrella Pine)

FUNGI: *Lactarius deliciosus; Suillus granulatus, luteus*

Great Britain 1503
Italy 1155
San Marino 1124

P. strobus (Weymouth or White Pine)

FUNGI: *Amanita caesarea, citrina, muscaria, rubescens; Cantharellus cibarius; Gyrodon merulioides; Gyroporus castaneus; Lactarius deliciosus; Lepiota rhacodes; Lepista nuda; Lycoperdon perlatum; Suillus bovinus, granulatus, luteus; Tylopilus felleus; Xerocomus subtomentosus*

Canada 879
United States of America 1737 2240

P. sylvestris (Scots Pine)

FUNGI: *Amanita citrina, muscaria, pantherina, phalloides, rubescens; Boletus edulis; Cantharellus cibarius, infundibuliformis; Clitopilus prunulus; Geastrum sessile; Gyromitra esculenta; Hebeloma crustuliniforme; Lactarius deliciosus; Leccinum aurantiacum, scabrum; Lepiota procera; Lycoperdon perlatum; Paxillus involutus; Pluteus cervinus; Rozites caperata; Russula cyanoxantha, decolorans, delica, paludosa, rubra, sanguinea, vesca; Suillus bovinus, granulatus, grevillei, luteus, variegatus; Tricholoma terreum; Tylopilus felleus; Xerocomus badius*

Andorra F326
Finland 724
Mongolia 1465
Poland 2559

ATANUS spp (The Planes)

FUNGUS: *Boletus edulis*

Bulgaria 1495 1496

POPULUS spp (The Poplars and Aspens)

P. alba (Abele or White Poplar)

FUNGUS: *Leccinum aurantiacum*

Poland 2558

P. tremula (Aspen or European Aspen)

FUNGI: *Clitopilus prunulus; Gyromitra esculenta; Leccinum aurantiacum, scabrum; Paxillus involutus; Russula delica, virescens*

Finland 754

P. tremuloides (American or Trembling Aspen)

FUNGI: *Leccinum aurantiacum, scabrum*

Canada 875
United States of America 2286

PRUNUS spp (Almonds, Cherries, Peaches and Plums)

P. spinosa (Blackthorn or Sloe)

FUNGI: *Hebeloma crustuliniforme; Tricholoma gambosum*

Germany (West Berlin) B585
Yugoslavia 1007

PSEUDOTSUGA spp (The Douglas Firs)

P. menziesii = *P. douglasii* = *P. taxifolia* (Oregon Douglas Fir)

FUNGI: *Amanita muscaria, pantherina; Boletus edulis, erythropus; Cantharellus cibarius; Hebeloma crustuliniforme; Hydnum repandum; Lactarius deliciosus, sanguifluus; Lycoperdon perlatum; Paxillus involutus; Russula delica; Suillus granulatus, luteus; Xerocomus subtomentosus*

Canada 876
United States of America 1363

PYRUS spp (The Pears)

P. communis (Common or Garden Pear)

FUNGI: *Marasmius scorodonius; Paxillus involutus*

Monaco 1875 1876 1877 1878 1952 1953 1954 1955

QUERCUS spp (The Oaks)

FUNGI: *Amanita muscaria; Boletus erythropus, luridus, regius; Cantharellus infundibuliformis; Clitopilus prunulus; Craterellus cornucopioides; Entoloma sinuata; Gyroporus castaneus; Hebeloma crustuliniforme; Leccinum aurantiacum; Lycoperdon perlatum; Paxillus involutus; Russula aurata, delica, sanguinea, vesca, virescens; Suillus bovinus, variegatus; Xerocomus subtomentosus*

Canada 878
Costa Rica 1023
Israel 825
Syria 711 731
United States of America 771 1740 2265 2329

Q. ilex (Evergreen or Holm Oak)

FUNGUS: *Amanita phalloides*

Spain 2146

Q. robur = *Q. pedunculata* (Common, English or Pedunculate Oak)

FUNGI: *Amanita caesarea, citrina, pantherina, phalloides, rubescens; Boletus edulis; Cantharellus cibarius; Lactarius piperatus; Leccinum scabrum; Russula cyanoxantha, paludosa; Tylopilus felleus; Xerocomus badius*

Bulgaria 1498
France 2691
Germany (West Germany) 1906
Great Britain 922
Liechtenstein 908
Poland 2557
Russia 5045
Sweden 283 284
Yugoslavia 1864 1864a

Q. suber (Cork Oak)

FUNGI: *Amanita caesarea, pantherina, phalloides; Boletus edulis; Lepiota procera; Russula rubra*

Portugal 1647

TILIA spp (The Limes or Lindens)

FUNGUS: *Leccinum scabrum*

Albania 701
Bulgaria 2916 3451
Japan 2004
Liechtenstein 377
Russia 5046

ULMUS spp (The Elms)

FUNGUS: *Hebeloma crustuliniforme*

France 2690
Guernsey 368

Stanley Gibbons Ltd

Head Office, Shop and Rare Stamp Departments
399 Strand, London WC2R 0LX.
Offices open Monday – Friday 9.30 a.m. to 5 p.m.
Shop open Monday 9.30 a.m. to 5.30 p.m., Tuesday – Friday 8.30 a.m. to 5.30 p.m. and
    Saturday 10 a.m. to 4.00 p.m.
Telephone 071-836 8444 and Telex 28883 for all departments.

Stanley Gibbons Publications
5, Parkside, Christchurch Road, Ringwood, Hants, BH24 3SH.
Telephone 0425 472363.